CW00408091

CONTENTS

Thanks are due to Peter Hillis and Paul Maloney of the University of Strathclyde, Faculty of Education, for compiling this guide.

© Scottish Consultative Council on the Curriculum 1997

First published 1997

ISBN 1 85955 135 1

INTRODUCTION

The aim of this guide is to provide teachers with information to help plan and resource the teaching of Scottish history within an overall history programme.

The guide includes a wide range of resource materials which concentrate on Scottish history and have been produced for schools. However, it should be noted that this is not intended as a comprehensive listing, but merely as an indication of some of the available commercial resources. It is appreciated that there will be worthwhile materials which are not included in the guide. The guide provides information on commercially produced materials which were available in May 1997 or shortly thereafter. It does not list the extensive range of resources held by libraries and museums for which further information can be obtained from specific libraries and museums, or by contacting the Scottish Centre for Information and Library Services and the Scottish Museums Council (see Section 7). Teachers should continue to seek and use a variety of sources and those identified in the guide will help schools develop their teaching of Scottish history.

Thanks are due to the organisations included in this guide for their generous help in providing materials and information. Please note that the publication dates and prices are accurate at the time of going to print.

If you have any comments or suggestions for future editions of this guide, or if you wish to obtain further copies, please contact:

Tegwen Wallace
Senior Information Officer
Scottish CCC
Gardyne Road
Broughty Ferry
Dundee DD5 1NY

Tel: 01382 455053

HOW TO USE THIS GUIDE

This guide has been divided into seven sections which list and describe various categories of resources:

- **Section 1** lists books and resource packs relevant to the teaching of Scottish history

- **Section 2** lists audio-visual materials

- **Section 3** describes a range of information technology based resources

- **Section 4** gives information on resources which help develop historical skills in the context of Standard Grade and Higher History

- **Section 5** gives details of organisations and publications to support Field Studies

- **Section 6**, entitled 'Further Support', contains addresses and contact numbers of various organisations which can provide support, materials and information to aid and develop the teaching of Scottish history

- **Section 7**, 'Obtaining Resources', lists the addresses of the publishers and suppliers of the resources listed in Sections 1–5.

An index of resource titles and series is included at the back of the guide.

Within Sections 1 and 3 resources are categorised under the chronological periods given within Environmental Studies 5–14, Understanding People in the Past:

- The Ancient World (pre-fifth century AD)
- The Middle Ages (400–1450)
- Renaissance, Reformation and The Age of Discovery (1450–1700)
- The Age of Revolutions (1700–1900)
- The Twentieth Century.

There is one additional category, **Various Periods**, which lists materials covering several of the above chronological periods. In each category resources are listed in ascending order according to pupil year group.

Entries in Sections 1, 2 and 3 provide information about the content of each resource, cross references to any supporting materials, and key publication/broadcast details (author, publisher/broadcaster, publication/broadcast date, ISBN, cost, medium and pupil audience).

LEARNING AND TEACHING SCOTTISH HISTORY

In February 1997 the Scottish CCC published a discussion and consultation paper, *Scottish History in the Curriculum*, prepared by the Scottish History Review Group. This report noted that Scottish history should be central to the history education delivered in Scottish schools and cited a number of reasons for this view. Scottish history has a personal and immediate relevance which makes it the starting point and reference for the study of history by people living in Scotland. Scottish history develops knowledge and understanding of the cultural inheritance bequeathed by past generations. Scottish history is also important for its role in fostering informed, responsible and active citizenship and for the opportunities it presents to develop certain vital skills, attitudes and dispositions.

However, history courses should not focus exclusively on Scottish history. They should develop an understanding of the world at large which requires a balance between local, Scottish, British, European and global themes. Scottish history should be taught in such a way as to exploit the full range of local and national resources available, including technology-based resources. It should be taught using a variety of approaches and learning activities, a view echoing the HM Inspector of Schools report into *Effective Learning and Teaching in Scottish Secondary Schools: History* published in 1992.

One recommendation of *Scottish History in the Curriculum* was that a resources strategy should be developed to support aspects of the teaching of history; that the Scottish CCC should facilitate the provision of resources to support Scottish history; and, in particular, that an annotated guide should be published, offering teachers advice on the full range of materials currently available to support the teaching of Scottish history. This guide results from that recommendation.

Section 1

Books and Resource Packs

The Romans in Scotland

An illustrated book giving an account of military and social features of the Roman period in Scotland (see also Section 2, page 35).

Author: Dargie, Richard
Publisher: BBC Education Scotland/Wayland Publishers
Publication Date: Spring 1998
ISBN: 075021550X
Cost: £10.99
Medium: Book
Pupil Audience: P4–P6

Settlers of Scotland

Part of the Understanding People in the Past series, designed to meet the requirements of the Scottish 5–14 curriculum in History, this examines the peoples of Scotland from the hunter gatherers, through the first metal workers, the Romans, Picts, Scots and Angles, early Christians and Vikings. The text includes activity panels with questions and exercises, and the combination of colour maps, illustrations, and photographs of sites and artefacts also includes comic strips and illustrated characters delivering text through speech bubbles. Organised in chronological sequence, with sections ranging from 10,000 to 1,200 years ago, chapters deal with most aspects of lifestyle, religion, and culture, and include such subjects as Living in a Neolithic House, Cairns of the Dead, Building and Living on the Antonine Wall, and the Holy Isle of Iona.

Series: Understanding People in the Past
Authors: Curtis, Elizabeth and Davidson, Kim
Publisher: Hodder and Stoughton Educational
Publication Date: 1996
ISBN: 0340655364
Cost: £4.99
Medium: Book
Pupil Audience: P4–P6

Ancient Scotland

This book describes the story of ancient Scotland from the Stone Age to the Romans. The straightforward and interesting text makes good use of primary evidence and contains many suggestions for pupil activities. The book is well illustrated with colour photographs and drawings of sites and artefacts. A teacher's guide and evaluation pack is also available for the series, which won the annual Times Educational Supplement (Scotland) award for books supporting the Scottish curriculum.

Please see the entry for a Sense of History, Scotland on page 28 for a description of the general series.

Series: A Sense of History, Scotland
Author: Morrison, Dorothy
Publisher: Addison Wesley Longman
Publication Date: 1996
ISBN: 0582261791
Cost: £26.99 for pack of 5
Medium: Book
Pupil Audience: P4–P7

The Celts: A Guide for Teachers

A teacher's pack that aims to introduce the topic of Iron Age peoples and to explain how we know about their lives from remaining evidence. Although some of the objects discussed and shown in illustrations will be displayed at the new Museum of Scotland, the pack is designed for use by teachers in all parts of the country. Its starting point is the carnyx – the boar-headed war trumpet found in North East Scotland – and it is divided into five main sections: A Brief Outline, Finding out the Evidence, Art and Technology, Warfare, and Belief, each of which includes a section suggesting ideas for activities. There are also sections on links to the 5–14 National Guidelines, further resources and photocopiable illustrations and carnyx mask. The pack is produced in black and white, loose-leaf A4 format.

Author: James, Alison
Publisher: National Museums of Scotland
Publication Date: 1996
Price: £2.00
Medium: Teacher's pack
Pupil Audience: P4–S2

Scotland in Roman Times

A history of the Romans in Scotland including information on the Roman Empire, army, fortifications in Scotland, Hadrian's Wall and the Antonine Wall. The text is illustrated with black and white sketches.

Author: Kamm, Antony
Publisher: Scottish Children's Press
Publication Date: September 1997
ISBN: 1899827145
Cost: £4.95
Medium: Book
Pupil Audience: P5–P7

The Ancient World

This book sets Scotland's early history into its wider European and world context. Chapters cover Scotland's first people, life in Roman Britain, the Great Empire of Alexander the Great and Ancient China. Each chapter contains photographs, diagrams, maps and suggested pupil activities.

Authors: Young, David and Wilson, Alan
Publisher: Imprint
Publication Date: 1996
ISBN: 1872035574
Cost: £4.95
Medium: Book
Pupil Audience: P6–S1

The Romans in Scotland

This imaginatively conceived full colour survey features chapters on the wild frontier, the Celts, the Roman Army in Scotland, the Battle of Mons, Graupius, Hadrian's Wall and the Antonine Wall. There are also chapters on the bath house, Roman food, health, technology, ships, transport and trade, while Trimontium – a Roman fort – gives insights into infrastructure. The illustrations are excellent and the general wit of the layout impressive. The informative text includes plenty of pupil activities, such as how to make a Roman helmet out of paper and card, a centrefold board game to encourage use of Roman numerals and a list of places to visit.

Series: Scottie Books
Author: Jarvie, Frances
Publisher: HMSO/National Museums of Scotland
Publication Date: 1994
ISBN: 0114942773
Cost: £4.50
Medium: Book
Pupil Audience: P6–S2

Neolithic and Bronze Age Scotland

A fairly detailed investigation of the first farmers in Scotland to the beginning of the Iron Age based on archaeological evidence. Well illustrated with reconstruction drawings, diagrams and photographs.

Author: Ashmore, Patrick
Publisher: Batsford/Historic Scotland
Publication Date: 1996
ISBN: 0713475315
Cost: £15.99
Medium: Book
Pupil Audience: S5–Certificate of Sixth Year Studies

Picts, Gaels and Scots

Drawing on the latest archaeological evidence and historical research, this book focuses on the contribution of the Picts and Gaels to the development of modern day Scotland. Well illustrated with reconstruction line drawings and photographs. Particularly useful for S5–S6 and for teachers looking for background information.

Author: Foster, Sally M.
Publisher: Batsford/Historic Scotland
Publication Date: 1996
ISBN: 0713474866
Cost: £15.99
Medium: Book
Pupil Audience: S5–Certificate of Sixth Year Studies

Prehistoric Orkney

This book shows how the prehistoric monuments in Orkney reveal the dwellings and everyday life of the early Orcadians, the rituals of life and death, the use of their settlements and tombs, and the tribal organisation involved in both building and ceremonies. Well illustrated with reconstruction drawings and photographs.

Author: Ritchie, Anna
Publisher: Batsford/Historic Scotland
Publication Date: 1995
ISBN: 0713475935
Price: £15.99
Medium: Book
Pupil Audience: S5–Certificate of Sixth Year Studies

Roman Scotland

A fairly detailed study of how the Roman Army set out to conquer Scotland and what effect their three invasions followed by three periods of occupation had on Scotland. Well illustrated with reconstruction drawings and photographs.

Author: Breeze, David J.
Publisher: Batsford/Historic Scotland
Publication Date: 1996
ISBN: 0713478896
Cost: £15.99
Medium: Book
Pupil Audience: S5–Certificate of Sixth Year Studies

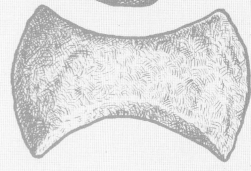

Scotland's First Settlers

A fairly detailed investigation of the hunter gatherers who lived in Scotland about 9,000 years ago before the establishment of settled farming. Well illustrated with reconstruction drawings and photographs.

Author: Wickham-Jones, C. R.
Publisher: Batsford/Historic Scotland
Publication Date: 1994
ISBN: 0713473711
Cost: £15.99
Medium: Book
Pupil Audience: S5–Certificate of Sixth Year Studies

Invaders of Scotland

An introduction to the archaeology of the Romans, Scots, Angles and Vikings, this offers chapters on each group, with texts combining detailed examination of specific sites with a general historical outline. The book is comprehensively illustrated with maps, diagrams and colour photographs of sites and artefacts. These include aerial shots of Jarlshof, Shetland, and useful sketches of the reconstruction of the Antonine Wall.

Authors: Ritchie, Anna and Breeze, David J.
Publisher: HMSO
Publication Date: 1996
ISBN: 011494136X
Cost: £4.95
Medium: Book
Pupil Audience: Not specific to any year group.

The Picts

This book provides a well illustrated introduction to the life of the Picts and the carved Pictish stones in the care of Historic Scotland. Chapters concentrate on 'Who Were the Picts?' 'Communication in Stone', 'The Art of Pictish Cross Slabs', 'Picts at Home and at War', and 'What Happened to the Picts?' Although the text is quite sophisticated, pupils could find useful information and illustrative material.

Authors: Ritchie, Anna
Publisher: HMSO
Publication Date: 1989
ISBN: 0114934916
Cost: £4.95
Medium: Book
Pupil Audience: Not specific to any year group.

Scotland BC

An introduction to prehistoric houses, tombs, ceremonial monuments and fortifications in the care of the Secretary of State for Scotland. Contents include: Houses of the Living, which features Skara Brae, Shetland houses, Jarlshof, earth-houses and wheelhouses; Houses of the Dead, Burial Monuments, which examines Cairnholy, cist burials, Cairnpapple and cemeteries; Circles and Cemeteries, which includes Kilmartin Valley, geometry, astronomy, and rock carving; and Strongholds High and Low, which includes sections on Shetland forts, brochs, Gurness, and Edin's Hall. The detailed but readable text is well illustrated with colour photographs of sites and artefacts.

Author: Ritchie, Anna
Publisher: HMSO
Publication Date: 1988
ISBN: 0114934274
Cost: £4.95
Medium: Book
Pupil Audience: Not specific to any year group.

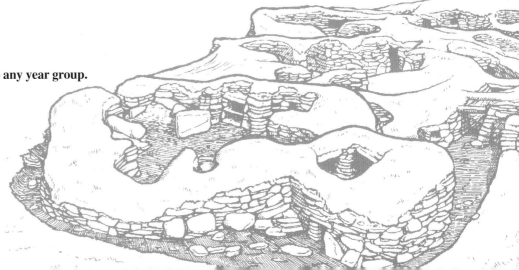

Celtic Journeys: Scotland in The Age of the Saints

This resource pack explores the travels, art, music, stories and religion of Scotland's Early Saints. Initiated to mark the anniversaries of Ninian and Columba in 1997, the pack covers many other famous and lesser known names associated with every part of Scotland.

The journeys of the Early Saints open up the geography of Scotland, and their settlements are an important clue to where we live now. The poetry, art, music, stories and sculptures of the Early Saints are central to Scotland's cultural identity and our place in Europe. The faith of the Early Saints is a spiritual legacy shared by all of Scotland's Christian Churches and admired by other religious traditions.

Everything in *Celtic Journeys* is designed for practical classroom use. It contains photocopiable worksheets and visual material. The materials are grouped according to age, with an easy-to-use framework which enables selection under 5–14 curriculum guidelines for Environmental Studies, Expressive Arts, English Language and Religious and Moral Education. *Celtic Journeys* also introduces some familiarisation with the use of Gaelic, and a Gaelic version of the pack is being developed by the Western Isles Council.

Author: Action of Churches Together in Scotland (ACTS)
Publisher: Scottish CCC
Publication Date: 1997
ISBN: 1859551238
Cost: £11.50
Medium: Resource pack
Pupil Audience: P3–P7; S1–S2 (discussion topics for S2 and beyond).

Robert the Bruce

This provides a clearly written narrative of the Bruce's campaigns, beginning with 'A Kingdom without a King', which explains the background to relations with England. The book's centrepiece is the two chapters on Bannockburn, and it is well illustrated throughout, particularly with colour photographs of castles and sites mentioned in the text. Includes a genealogical tree, glossary and timeline.

Series: Scottish History Topics
Author: Rasmusen, Barbara Mure
Publisher: Heinemann
Publication Date: 1996
ISBN: 0431078718
Cost: £7.99
Medium: Book
Pupil Audience: P3–P5

A Separate Kingdom

Part of the Understanding People in the Past series and designed to meet the requirements of the Scottish 5–14 curriculum in History, this is divided into three sections: Making a Kingdom, which begins with Who Lived in Scotland 1,000 Years Ago, and covers Malcolm, King David and the birth of Scottish nationhood; Defending a Kingdom, which deals with Wallace, Bruce and the Wars of Independence; and Living in a Kingdom which includes life in a castle, life in a medieval town and life for the monks of Melrose. The text includes activity sections, colour illustrations, maps and photographs, as well as comic strips and characters with speech bubbles.

Series: Understanding People in the Past
Author: McKichan, Findlay
Publisher: Hodder and Stoughton Educational
Publication Date: 1996
ISBN: 0340655372
Cost: £4.99
Medium: Book
Pupil Audience: P4–P6

The Vikings in Scotland

Opening with a description of the attack on Iona in 795 AD, early chapters cover the origins of the Norse peoples, their settlement in Scotland, and the Dark Ages, with a separate entry on the Orkney Jarls. Later sections focus on Viking lifestyle and culture, including feasting and sagas, Norse mythology, the role of women, and longships. Well illustrated with photographs, maps and coloured illustrations, this also discusses the Norse legacy in words and place names. (See also Section 2, page 33)

Author: Dargie, Richard
Publisher: BBC Education Scotland/Wayland Publishers
Publication Date: 1996
ISBN: 0750215704
Cost: £10.99
Medium: Book
Pupil Audience: P4–P6

The Wars of Independence

A well illustrated and clearly written account of life and events from Alexander III to the Declaration of Arbroath. The book combines colour photographs, maps and illustrations with good use of primary evidence, together with suggested activities for pupils. A teacher's guide and evaluation pack for the series is available. The series won the annual Times Educational Supplement (Scotland) award for books supporting the Scottish curriculum.

Please see the entry for 'A Sense of History, Scotland' on page 28 for a description of the general series.

Series: A Sense of History, Scotland
Author: Morrison, Dorothy
Publisher: Addison Wesley Longman
Publication Date: 1996
ISBN: 0582261813
Cost: £26.99 per pack of 5
Medium: Book
Pupil Audience: P4–P7

Chuck Wallace's Middle Age Spread

Support materials to accompany Channel 4 series on Scotland in the time of Wallace and Bruce (see page 33 for programming details). As at May 1997 there was no further information about this publication.

Publisher: Channel 4 Learning
Publication Date: 1998
Cost: £3.95
Medium: Teacher's guide to support television series
Pupil Audience: P5–P7

Fyvie Castle – Its Life and Legends

This resource pack is based on the life and legends associated with Fyvie Castle. It covers battles, castles, folklore, art and design, mapping and social history. The materials can be used in whole or in parts. The whole pack takes approximately three months to complete and covers nearly every aspect of Environmental Studies 5–14.

Authors: Monquitter, Fintry, Rothienorman and King Edward Primary Schools
Publisher: Aberdeenshire Council
Publication Date: 1997
Cost: £40.00
Medium: Resource pack
Pupil Audience: P5–P7

Robert Bruce: Scotland's Hero King (differentiated edition)

Differentiated text version of *Bruce's Scotland* (see entry below).

Author: Stephen, Margaret
Publisher: BBC Education Scotland/Wayland Publishers
Publication Date: 1995
ISBN: 075021547X
Cost: £9.99
Medium: Book
Pupil Audience: P5–P7

Wallace, Bruce and The War of Independence

This book describes the key events surrounding the Scottish War of Independence, focusing on the campaigns of Wallace and Bruce. Chapter headings include: The Golden Age of Alexander III, The Guardians of Scotland, William Wallace, The Battle of Stirling Bridge, Robert the Bruce, The Battle of Bannockburn – Day 1, The Battle of Bannockburn – Day 2, and What Happened Next? The book is illustrated with black and white drawings and maps depicting the position of both armies at Stirling Bridge and Bannockburn. There are also more general maps of Scotland. The readable text makes this book suitable for either classroom use or more general reading.

Authors: Kamm, Antony
Publisher: Scottish Children's Press
Publication date: 1997
ISBN: 1899827153
Cost: £4.95
Medium: Book
Pupil Audience: P5–P7

Bruce's Scotland

Opening chapters describe Scotland in the late thirteenth century, its different peoples and languages, its feudal society, trade and the Burghs, and the Scottish Church. Subsequent chapters provide a lucid narrative of events from the death of Alexander III to the Declaration of Arbroath. Other features include maps and descriptions of the battles of Stirling Bridge and Bannockburn, and comparisons between English and Scottish soldiers' weaponry and tactics. Like others in this series, it is well illustrated. (See also Section 2, page 34).

Author: Spankie, Mari
Publisher: BBC Education Scotland/Wayland Publishers
Publication Date: 1994
ISBN: 0750212322
Cost: £9.99
Medium: Book
Pupil Audience: P6–S2

Robert the Bruce: A Scots Life

A Scots language biography aimed at younger and new readers in Scots. Includes a glossary and black and white illustrations.

Series: Scots Legends
Author: Telfer, Glenn
Publisher: Argyll Publishing
Publication Date: 1996
ISBN: 1874640521
Cost: £6.99
Medium: Book
Pupil Audience: P6–S2

Saints of Scotland

Beginning with 'What is a Saint?' this full colour book includes chapters on a wide range of Scottish figures, including Ninian, Columba, the Saints of the Western Isles, Serf, Kentigern, Fergus and MacLean, the Saints of the North-East, Kenneth, the two Fillans, Triduaria, Cuthbert of Melrose and Lindisfarne, Adrian, Baldied, Ebba, and the two Royal Saints, Margaret and David. There is also a chapter on 'The Saint-less Years', which provides background on the Reformation, and the well written text includes plenty of imaginative tasks and activities for pupils, such as playing Viking chequers and making their own illustrated manuscript. The middle centrefold 'The Great Glen Adventure' is a board game based on Columba's journey from Iona to Inverness. Includes a list of places to visit.

Series: Scottie Books
Author: Dunlop, Eileen
Publisher: HMSO/National Museums of Scotland
Publication Date: 1996
ISBN: 0114952515
Cost: £4.50
Medium: Book
Pupil Audience: P6–S2

Scotland's Vikings

This addition to the Scottie Books series is due for publication in September 1997.

Series: Scottie Books
Authors: Jarvie, Frances and Gordon
Publisher: HMSO/National Museums of Scotland
Publication Date: 1997
ISBN: 0114958130
Cost: £4.99
Medium: Book
Pupil Audience: P6–S2

William Wallace: A Scots Life

A Scots language biography intended for younger and new readers in Scots. Includes glossary and black and white illustrations.

Series: Scots Legends
Author: Telfer, Glenn
Publisher: Argyll Publishing
Publication Date: 1995
ISBN: 1874640467
Cost: £6.99
Medium: Book
Pupil Audience: P6–S2

Life in the Times of Wallace and Bruce

Pack of teaching materials. Contents include booklets on documents on Scotland in the days of Wallace and Bruce; life in the country; the royal burgh; the Church; food at the time of Wallace and Bruce, together with blank maps of Scotland and a board game, 'A Message to the King'. For two topics, castles and communications, separate booklets are provided for three different ability levels (A – below average; B – average; C – above average). Well illustrated with black and white sketches, particularly vigorous in the sections on castle sieges. Includes teacher's introduction.

Authors: Cuthbert, M. M. G.; Morrison, D. J. A.; Halliday, J. and Taylor, W.
Publisher: Northern College
Publication Date: 1979
Cost: £3.50 and £1.00 p+p
Medium: Resource pack
Pupil Audience: P7–S1

Scotland in the Times of Wallace and Bruce

Ring-bound format includes sections on investigating Wallace and Bruce; life in the country; the royal burgh; the Church; food; communications; castles; and primary sources. The activity orientated text includes a wide variety of questions and exercises, and is well illustrated with black and white maps, drawings and diagrams. Also includes teacher's notes and maps of Scotland.

Author: Doig, Robert
Publisher: Northern College
Publication Date: 1996
Cost: £40.00
Medium: Teaching pack and ring binder
Pupil Audience: P7–S1

Scotland in the Middle Ages

An imaginatively laid out chronological history that includes social, political and economic factors. Subject units are sub-divided into single page topics headed by questions in bold type, for example, 'Why was David I a Great King?' and 'What did a Burgh look like?' Responses combine text, visual material, views of modern historians and a Things to Do section. Units cover early peoples of Scotland, the Vikings, the coming of Christianity, Alba, the Normans, the Medieval Church, life in burghs and in the countryside, the wars with England and the Stewart dynasty. Black and white only.

Author: Dargie, Richard
Publisher: Pulse Publications
Publication Date: 1995
ISBN: 0948766360
Cost: £6.95
Medium: Book
Pupil Audience: P7–S2

Scottish Life Before 1500

The text combines maps, black and white photographs and diagrams with original source material, and includes panels suggesting questions and exercises to test comprehension. With initial chapters on hunters, settlers, strange beliefs and metal users, this goes on to cover the Roman invasion, Picts, early Christianity, the Vikings, Scots and Normans, Wallace, Bruce and Bannockburn. Later chapters examine castles, royal burghs, monastic orders, and life in the countryside, the Highlands, and the Borders.

Author: Wood, Sydney
Publisher: Stanley Thornes (Publishers) Ltd
Publication Date: 1986
ISBN: 0748722599
Cost: £5.99
Medium: Book
Pupil Audience: P7–S2

Freedom is a Noble Thing: Scottish Independence 1286–1329

This booklet was produced for the summer 1996 exhibition of the same title and contains extracts and copies of documents covering the period. Other titles on a variety of topics are available in the History At Source series. Their contents generally consist of excerpts from letters and documents, interspersed with black and white reproductions and facsimile manuscript pages of accounts and registers. Intended to be used in conjunction with textbooks, the booklets include bibliographies and sections on further information.

Series: History At Source
Publisher: Scottish Record Office, Edinburgh
Publication Date: 1996
Cost: £3.50
Medium: Primary source booklet
Pupil Audience: Standard Grade/Higher

Scottish Abbeys and Priories

The medieval abbeys and priories are among the most inspiring buildings ever built on Scottish soil. This book brings to life the rich and varied history and architecture of Scotland's monastic orders. Good illustrations and photographs.

Author: Fawcett, Richard
Publisher: Batsford/Historic Scotland
Publication Date: 1994
ISBN: 071347372X
Cost: £15.99
Medium: Book
Pupil Audience: S5–Certificate of Sixth Year Studies

The Early Stewart Kings, Robert II and Robert III, 1371–1406

A scholarly biography of the two kings which examines the way in which their poor reputations grew from later embellishments to contemporary political propaganda. Contains material of possible use for the Certificate of Sixth Year Studies.

Series: The Stewart Dynasty in Scotland
Author: Boardman, Stephen
Publisher: Tuckwell Press
Publication Date: 1996
ISBN: 1898410437
Cost: £14.99
Medium: Book
Pupil Audience: Certificate of Sixth Year Studies

James I

Full length biography of possible use for the Certificate of Sixth Year Studies.

Series: The Stewart Dynasty in Scotland
Author: Brown, Michael
Publisher: Tuckwell Press
Publication Date: 1994
ISBN: 1898410402
Cost: £12.99
Medium: Book
Pupil Audience: Certificate of Sixth Year Studies

Medieval Scotland: Sources for the 12th Century

Number 20 in Scottish CCC's Curriculum Support Series provides materials to support the Medieval Society section of the General Study in Revised Higher Grade History.

The sources have been grouped under four headings and presented as four separate A4 booklets:

(i) *Those Who Fought*
(ii) *Those Who Ploughed*
(iii) *Those Who Prayed*
(iv) *Towns*.

The collection is designed for flexible use. Some of the sections are a straightforward read; others are structured for individual or group work with questions and discussion points. A short bibliography is included so that students can readily follow up points of interest.

Series: Curriculum Support Series: 20
Author: Hamilton, E. C.
Publisher: Scottish CCC
Publication Date: 1995
ISBN: 20(i) 1859550614
        20(ii) 1859550622
        20(iii) 1859550630
        20(iv) 1859550649
Cost: 20(i) £4.50
        20(ii) £2.50
        20(iii) £2.50
        20(iv) £2.50
Medium: 20(i) A4 booklet (62 pp)
        20 (ii) A4 booklet (20 pp)
        20 (iii) A4 booklet (36 pp)
        20 (iv) A4 booklet (25 pp)
Pupil Audience: Certificate of Sixth Year Studies

The Wars of the Bruces: Scotland, England and Ireland, 1306–1328

A narrative account that demonstrates how Bruce's war with England affected the whole of the British Isles. Of possible use for the Certificate of Sixth Year Studies/Advanced Higher.

Author: McNamee, Colm
Publisher: Tuckwell Press
Publication Date: 1997
ISBN: 1898410925
Cost: £14.99
Medium: Book
Pupil Audience: Certificate of Sixth Year Studies/ Advanced Higher

Mary Queen of Scots

This covers the events and personalities of Mary's life from childhood to her execution. The clearly written narrative text is well illustrated with drawings, paintings, maps and colour photographs, and includes primary and secondary source material. The book also includes a timeline and glossary.

Series: Scottish History Topics
Author: Rasmusen, Barbara Mure
Publisher: Heinemann
Publication Date: 1996
ISBN: 043107870X
Cost: £7.99
Medium: Book
Pupil Audience: P3–P5

A Queen's Promise: A Tale of Mary Queen of Scots

Children's historical adventure story set near Dumfries. When their father's horse dies, throwing the family into poverty, James and Meg decide to approach Queen Mary, who is staying at nearby Caerlaverock Castle, to ask for her help. Includes black and white line drawings and short historical notes on Mary Queen of Scots, John Knox, life in the time of Queen Mary, and the Scots language.

Author: White, Kirsty
Publisher: Franklin Watts
Publication Date: 1997
ISBN: 0749625899
Cost: £6.99
Medium: Book
Pupil Audience: P4–P6

Dynasty: A Guide for Teachers

Aimed at helping prepare for a visit to the exhibition 'Dynasty: The Royal House of Stewart' at the Scottish National Portrait Gallery, the pack has two main themes: Mary Queen of Scots, and the Jacobites. Each theme has a family tree, and sections on the historical context, key paintings, key objects, and things to do, both in the classroom and at the exhibition. It also contains sections on links to the 5–14 Guidelines, an exhibition plan practical information and photocopiable illustrated material. Black and white.

Author: Small, Ewan
Publisher: National Museums of Scotland
Publication Date: 1995
Cost: £2.00
Medium: Resource pack
Pupil Audience: P4–S2

Mary, Queen of Scots

This imaginatively produced full colour book provides chapters on the key events and personalities of Mary's life. The illustrations are excellent and the clear informative text features a wide range of stimulating puzzles and activities, including making your own family tree and a 'Race for the Throne' board game. Includes a list of places to visit.

Author: Douglas, Elizabeth
Publisher: HMSO/National Museums of Scotland
Publication Date: 1994
ISBN: 011494265X
Cost: £4.50
Medium: Book
Pupil Audience: P6–S2

Scottish Castles

This imaginatively produced full colour activity book provides separate chapters on the history and legends of a wide variety of castles. Those featured are: Edinburgh, Dumbarton, Stirling, Caerlaverock, St Andrews, Threave, Craigmillar, Doune, Ferniehurst, Dunvegan, Crathes, Thirlestane, Drumlanrig, Culzean and Balmoral. There are also opening chapters on 'Scotland – A Land of Castles' and 'The Brochs'. Chapters on 'Inside Edinburgh Castle 1566' and 'The Lochleven Castle Estates 1590' provide insights into the internal workings of castle life. The wide range of tasks and activities include making a model siege catapult out of a milk carton.

Series: Scottie Books
Author: Jarvie, Gordon
Publisher: HMSO/National Museums of Scotland
Publication Date: 1995
ISBN: 0114942765
Cost: £4.50
Medium: Book
Pupil Audience: P6–S2

James IV: A Renaissance King

A well written and readable narrative account. The seven chapters are: The Boyhood of James IV; The Battle of Sauchieburn; James IV – A Strong King; Rebellion in the North, which covers the Highland/Lowland divide, the clan system and James' suppression of the MacDonalds; James' Kingdom, which includes sections on the village, the burgh, the Church and the court; England, Friend or Foe; James – A Renaissance King, which assesses the achievements of James' reign in the context of the wider European Renaissance, focusing on education, printing, science, medicine, buildings and literature; and Flodden, which provides a detailed account of the battle. The book is particularly well illustrated with colour photographs of sites and artefacts, maps, paintings and drawings.

Authors: Blackie, Ruth; Donaldson; Graham; and MacKenzie, Douglas
Publisher: Canongate Books Ltd
Publication Date: 1996
ISBN: 0862416396
Cost: £8.99
Medium: Book
Pupil Audience: P7–S2

Life in Sixteenth-Century Scotland

This pack folds out into 12 A3 sheets headed: The Queen's Council; Parliament; Hearing the News; The Country (1 and 2); The Town (1 and 2); At Home; Things to Buy; Clothes and Food; Learning and Writing; and New Ideas. The contents include illustrations and extracts from documents and primary source material, some of it in Scots. They also include notes on using the resource pack, and on the language of the documents, together with some practical ideas for further study, a list of difficult words and some sources of further information.

Publisher: Scottish Record Office
Author: Sanderson, Margaret H. B.
Publication Date: 1988
Cost: £3.25
Medium: Resource pack
Pupil Audience: P7–S2

Mary Stuart

The readable text combines a narrative account of the events of Mary's life with integrated chapters on changes in the Church (explaining the background to the Scottish Reformation and the importance of religion), John Knox, Mary and the Reformers, and the royal burgh of Edinburgh. The book is particularly well illustrated with drawings, engravings and colour maps, paintings and photographs of sites.

Author: Hunter, John
Publisher: Canongate Books Ltd
Publication Date: 1996
ISBN: 0862416418
Cost: £8.99
Medium: Book
Pupil Audience: P7–S2

Montrose: Covenanter, Royalist and Man of Principle

A clearly written narrative account that includes chapters on: Montrose's youth, how people lived, James VI, Charles I and religion (which explains the religious context and the background to the Covenant), the Bishops' Wars, King Stewart or King Campbell?, Annus Mirabilis (on the campaigns of 1644–5 and the defeat at Philiphaugh), exile, and the last campaign. The layout is well provided with coloured subheadings and the book is particularly well illustrated with colour photographs, maps, paintings and drawings.

Author: Blackie, Ruth
Publisher: Canongate Books Ltd
Publication Date: 1996
ISBN: 086241640X
Cost: £8.99
Medium: Book
Pupil Audience: P7–S2

Scottish Life 1500–1750

This includes short excerpts from original source material and panels suggesting tests and exercises to test pupils' comprehension. The first two sections, 'Troubled Times' and 'Union Issues', cover the narrative of events. The third, 'Daily Life', includes chapters on Highland life, burgh life, a visit to Edinburgh, rich and poor, exploring industries, women's issues and crime and punishment. Illustrated with black and white photographs, maps, drawings and diagrams.

Author: Wood, Sydney
Publisher: Stanley Thornes (Publishers) Ltd
Publication Date: 1995
ISBN: 0748720863
Cost: £5.99
Medium: Book
Pupil Audience: P7–S2

King or Covenant? Voices from Civil War

This book provides biographical studies of 13 people from the middle ranks of society, derived from memoirs, diaries or letters, reconstructing their characters and showing how their lives were affected by Scotland's mid-seventeenth century wars. Of possible use for the Certificate of Sixth Year Studies.

Author: Stevenson, David
Publisher: Tuckwell Press
Publication Date: 1996
ISBN: 189841081X
Cost: £14.99
Medium: Book
Pupil Audience: Certificate of Sixth Year Studies

Scotland: Reformation to Restoration

This annotated bibliography was compiled to support the Certificate of Sixth Year Studies (CSYS) field of study on Scotland: Reformation to Restoration. It includes details of primary and secondary sources covering James VI's reign, the Reformation and Settlement, Mary Queen of Scots, Charles I and the Covenanters and the Cromwellian occupation and union.

Series: Curriculum Support Series 16 (i)
Author: Kirk, J.
Publisher: Scottish CCC
Publication Date: 1993
ISBN: 1859550045
Cost: £2.00
Medium: Booklet
Pupil Audience: Certificate of Sixth Year Studies

A Queen's Progress

Subtitled 'An Introduction to the Buildings Associated with Mary Queen of Scots in the Care of the Secretary of State for Scotland', this examines Mary's life with special reference to the buildings in which the events of her reign took place. It is well illustrated with colour photographs and paintings, mainly of portraits and the various castles and palaces, notably Linlithgow Palace, Lochleven Castle, and Dundrennan Abbey. The book includes a narrative account of Mary's life with detailed examination of the buildings' history and architectural features.

Author: Breeze, David J.
Publisher: HMSO
Publication Date: 1987
ISBN: 011493343X
Cost: £3.50
Medium: Book
Pupil Audience: Not specific to any year group.

Scottish Castles and Fortifications

This authoritative survey combines a detailed but readable text with excellent colour illustrations and photographs, including some striking aerial shots. Opening chapters on the castle as residence and the castle as fortress provide detailed accounts of the social organisation and domestic conditions of castle life, and outline the increasing sophistication of castles' defensive features. Later chapters form a chronological sequence, and include: The First Castles; Castles of the Kings of Peace; The Thirteenth Century; The Aftermath of War; Robert I to James I; Castle and Cannon; James II to Mary; King James VI's Peace; and Public Works and Private Homes.

Author: Tabraham, Christopher
Publisher: HMSO
Year of Publication: 1986
ISBN: 0114924759
Cost: £3.95
Medium: Book
Pupil Audience: Not specific to any year group.

Bonnie Prince Charlie

This uses a clearly written and informative text, together with excellent colour illustrations, to provide a strong narrative account of the '45. The layout includes maps, paintings and colour photographs of castles and landscapes featured in the story. While the factual content of earlier sections concerning the military campaign is impressive, the quotations of the Skye Boat Song and recounting of the story of Flora MacDonald in the later chapters reinforces the romantic aspects of the story. The book also contains a glossary and timeline.

Series: Scottish History Topics
Author: Rasmusen, Barbara Mure
Publisher: Heinemann
Publication Date: 1996
ISBN: 0431078734
Cost: £7.99
Medium: Book
Pupil Audience: P3–P5

A Dream of Danger: The Massacre of Glencoe

Children's historical adventure story. Morag, granddaughter of the Chief of Clanranald, goes to stay with her aunt in Glencoe and experiences dreams and premonitions of danger that allow her to warn some of the MacDonalds of the massacre. Includes line drawings and brief historical notes on the massacre, the Glorious Revolution, the Bards and second sight.

Author: White, Kirsty
Publisher: Franklin Watts
Publication Date: 1997
ISBN: 0749625872
Cost: £6.99
Medium: Book
Pupil Audience: P4–P6

Over the Sea to Skye: A Tale of Bonnie Prince Charlie

Enjoyable historical adventure story in which Maggie, daughter of the Chieftain of the MacDonnells of Glenaffin, helps Prince Charlie evade the Redcoats and escape to Skye dressed in her clothes. Includes black and white illustrations and short historical notes on Bonnie Prince Charlie, Flora MacDonald, the Jacobites and Highland dress.

Author: White, Kirsty
Publisher: Franklin Watts
Publication Date: 1997
ISBN: 0749625880
Cost: £6.99
Medium: Book
Pupil Audience: P4–P6

Scotland in the Time of Burns

This examines Burns' life and work in the wider context of the society in which he lived. The 20 chapter headings, covering industry (linen, mills, transport), popular culture, politics and religion, are intended to show how Burns' work reflected the changing balance of society, and are interspersed with examples of his poems and writings. Concluding chapters on the Burns legacy and the land of Burns, stress the poet's enduring place in Scottish culture. Well illustrated with colour photographs, maps, paintings and drawings. Supports BBC Scotland's education series on Burns (see page 37).

Authors: Rose, Iain and Gunn, Donald
Publisher: Canongate Books Ltd
Publication Date: 1996
ISBN: 0862416388
Cost: £8.99
Medium: Book
Pupil Audience: P4–P6

A Stranger in the Glen: A Tale About Rob Roy

A children's adventure story. When Rob Roy MacGregor wants to charge her father 100 merks for letting his cattle through to market, Catriona and her young brother Rory decide to get up in the middle of the night and take the cattle to market themselves. This book includes line drawings and short notes on Scotland in Rob Roy's time, life in the Highlands, Rob Roy and Gaelic.

Author: White, Kirsty
Publisher: Franklin Watts
Publication Date: 1997
ISBN: 0749625864
Cost: £6.99
Medium: Book
Pupil Audience: P4–P6

Highland Clearances

A well illustrated colour survey, with sections headed: The Highlands (with background on the clan system); Change in the Highlands; Sheep not People; The Sutherland Clearances; The Potato Famine; Queen Victoria; and What Happened to the Highlanders? The clearly written text draws on primary evidence, such as eyewitness accounts of the Sutherland Clearances, and includes suggested activities for pupils. A teacher's book and evaluation pack for the series is available. The series won the annual Times Educational Supplement (Scotland) award for books supporting the Scottish curriculum.

See the entry for 'A Sense of History, Scotland' on page 28 for a description of the general series.

Series: A Sense of History Scotland
Authors: Purkis, Sally and Mason, James
Publisher: Addison Wesley Longman
Publication Date: 1996
ISBN: 0582261988
Cost: £22.50 for pack of 5
Medium: Book
Pupil Audience: P4–P7

The Highland Clearances

A well illustrated colour survey which covers the history of the Clearances from the Ross-shire Sheep Riot to the Crofters' War. It includes background chapters on the Union with England, the clan system, and the Jacobite rebellions, and on the Sutherland Clearances and emigration and famine. Other chapters address such questions as 'Why was there no revolution?' and 'Where did the people go?' The clearly written text includes primary source material and is well illustrated with colour and black and white archive photographs, maps, diagrams and drawings.

Authors: Gunn, Donald and Spankie, Mari
Publisher: BBC Education Scotland/Wayland Publishers
Publication Date: 1993
ISBN: 0750207531
Cost: £9.99
Medium: Book. Links to computer program, *The Clearances*, produced by the BBC and the Scottish Council for Educational Technology.
Pupil Audience: P4–S2

Also available in paperback
ISBN: 0750214139
Cost: £5.99

The Jacobites

Well illustrated account of the Jacobite risings, which includes socio-political background material on the Act of Union and the clan system. Also includes maps and diagrams of battles, together with some quotations from Gaelic sources.

Author: Rose, Iain
Publisher: Wayland Publishers Ltd
Publication Date: 1995
ISBN: 075021516X
Cost: £10.99
Medium: Book
Pupil Audience: P4–S2

Also available in paperback
ISBN: 0750221925
Cost: £5.99

Life During The Highland Clearances (differentiated edition)

Differentiated text version of *The Highland Clearances*.

Author: Stephen, Margaret
Publisher: BBC Education Scotland/Wayland Publishers
Publication Date: 1995
ISBN: 0750215321
Cost: £9.99
Medium: Book
Pupil Audience: P5–P7

The Jacobites

Teacher's guide to support the Channel 4 series (see page 34 for programming details). The guide provides a synopsis of each programme and highlights key questions within them. It includes suggestions for activities both before and after watching and photocopiable worksheets for each programme. The guide is produced in black and white.

Author: McRobbie, Maura
Publisher: Channel 4 Learning Ltd
Publication Date: 1995
ISBN: 1899214739
Cost: £3.95
Medium: Teacher's guide to support television series
Pupil Audience: P5–S1

Robert Burns: Alive and Kicking

Teacher's guide to accompany the Channel 4 series on Burns' life and poetry (see page 34 for programming details). The guide provides a synopsis to each programme and includes suggestions for activities both before and after watching, together with photocopiable activity sheets. It also contains a chronology of Burns' life and background material on eighteenth-century Scotland. Illustrated with maps and black and white drawings. The series is due to be broadcast in Autumn 1997, with the transmission of the first programme currently scheduled for 26 September. It is also available on five 50-minute videos from Channel 4 Schools.

Author: McRobbie, Maura
Publisher: Channel 4 Learning Ltd
Publication Date: 1996
ISBN: 1862150141
Cost: £3.95
Medium: Teacher's guide to support television series
Pupil Audience: P6–S1

Children of Coal and Iron

Opening chapters examine coal mining and iron-making processes in the early nineteenth century, with special reference to conditions experienced by child workers. Other chapters cover the increase in demand for coal and iron, the growth of new industrial towns, mine owners, and social issues such as housing, health, education, accidents, and the reforms contained in the 1842 Mines Act. Particularly well illustrated with maps, engravings and archive photographs, this also includes contemporary children's eyewitness accounts from the 1842 Report.

Authors: Rose, Iain and MacLean, Donald
Publisher: Wayland Publishers Ltd
Publication Date: 1996
ISBN: 0750217898
Cost: £11.99
Publication Date: Book
Pupil Audience: P6–S2

The Jacobites

This imaginative, full colour book opens with 'What is a Jacobite?' and Highland life, and goes on to provide chapters on most events and personalities from Bonnie Dundee and Sheriffmuir, to Culloden and after the '45 Rebellion. The excellent layout includes an informative text and a wide range of questions and activities that range from breaking the code of a Jacobite letter, a 'Rob Roy' game and a recipe for making oatcakes. Includes a list of places to visit.

Series: Scottie Books
Author: Kamm, Antony
Publisher: HMSO/National Museums of Scotland
Publication Date: 1995
ISBN: 0114952507
Cost: £4.50
Medium: Book
Pupil Audience: P6–S2

The Union of 1707

Combines an account of the events and personalities of 1707 with a broader examination of the constitutional, political and economic background and consequences for Scotland. The text includes chapters on Scottish-English relations prior to James I/VI, the religious differences between the two countries, the Company of Scotland, and the Darien disaster as well as the Articles of Union and the Union today. Well illustrated.

Author: Rose, Iain
Publisher: Wayland Publishers Ltd
Publication Date: 1996
ISBN: 0750217480
Cost: £10.99
Medium: Book
Pupil Audience: P6–S2

Victorian Scotland

A general text covering the main aspects of Victorian Scotland, including Victoria's Scotland, city life, education and Victorian style. As with other Wayland publications this book is very well illustrated and includes a glossary and suggested places to visit. The book provides a comprehensive overview of the Victorians with the panoramic photograph of Loch Katrine illustrating one lasting legacy of the Victorians to the West of Scotland.

Author: Foley, Kathryn
Publisher: Wayland Publishers Ltd
Publication Date: 1997
ISBN: 0750219629
Cost: £10.99
Publication Date: Book
Pupil Audience: P6–S2

The Coalminers

A well produced large format compilation of archive photographs and extracts from documents and primary source material held by the Scottish Records Offices. Its six sections cover the pits, serfdom, working conditions, women and children, housing, and welfare. Documents reproduced range from an indenture of apprenticeship from 1767, a statement of the Combination Laws of 1799–1800, and conditions of work at Donibristle Colliery in Fife (nineteenth century), to women and girls' evidence given before the Enquiry of 1842, and instructions to horsekeepers at Blantyre Colliery, Lanarkshire in 1891. Black and white.

Publisher: Scottish Record Office
Publication Date: 1983
Cost: £3.00
Medium: Book (Archive Unit)
Pupil Audience: P7–S2

The Jacobites

This book examines the background to the Jacobite Rebellion with particular emphasis on events before, during and after the 1745 Rebellion. Supporting information includes chapters on the building of forts and roads throughout the Highlands. The book contains sketches and maps alongside pupil tasks.

Authors: Rose, Iain and Andrew, Hugh
Publisher: C. B. Publishing Ltd
Publication Date: 1990
ISBN: 1872985009
Cost: £4.00
Medium: Book
Pupil Audience: P7–S2

The Jacobites

This pack comprises ten A3 sheets with the headings: Who Were the Jacobites?; Sheriffmuir; Prince Charlie Arrives; The Prince in Edinburgh; Prestonpans; To England and Back; Falkirk and Retreat; Culloden; and After the '45 parts 1 and 2. Contents consist of excerpts from a wide range of original documents, together with facsimiles and illustrations, and a sheet giving section by section ideas for further study. Black and white illustrations.

Publisher: Scottish Record Office, Edinburgh
Publication Date: 1988
Cost: £3.25
Medium: Resource pack
Pupil Audience: P7–S2

The Scottish Railway Story

A well produced large format compilation of archive photographs, posters, timetables and documents drawn from the Scottish Railway Archives. Divided into four parts (The Coming of the Railways, The Companies' Servants, The Travellers, and The Trains), this includes facsimiles of letters, drawings and records, as well as outstanding photographs, and constitutes a social history of the railways in Scotland. Black and white.

Publisher: Scottish Record Office
Publication Date: 1992
ISBN: 0114941874
Cost: £6.95
Medium: Book (Archive Unit)
Pupil Audience: P7–S2

Victorian Scotland

Part of the Understanding People in the Past series, developed to meet the requirements of the Scottish 5–14 curriculum in History, this book contrasts life and work for different sections of society. The colourful layout, which features maps, photographs and paintings, includes illustrated characters delivering text through voice bubbles, as well as activity panels suggesting questions and exercises. Section headings cover At Home, At Work, Spare Time, Travel, In Trouble, and Changing Times. Within these sections, individual chapters generally concentrate on immediate conditions ('Inside a Wealthy Home', 'Which Job will you Choose?') but also include separate entries for the Glasgow Exhibition of 1901, the Tay Bridge Disaster, and the split in the Church, as well as themes such as women's equality.

Series: Understanding People in the Past
Author: Wood, Sydney
Publisher: Hodder and Stoughton Educational
Publication Date: 1996
ISBN: 0340655380
Cost: £4.99
Medium: Book
Pupil Audience: P7–S2

Changing Life in Scotland and Britain 1750–1850

Part of the Standard Grade History series, this makes extensive use of diverse primary and secondary source material, together with well presented statistical data. Illustrated with paintings, engravings, photos, maps and diagrams, the black and white layout also features activity panels offering questions, exercises, and suggested topics for group work. Chapters cover population, agriculture, transport, industry, the growth of towns, the drive for democracy, the Church in charge, and the New Town, with short opening and closing sections on Scotland in 1750 and 1850. Chapters are divided into two sections, the first aimed at General and Upper Foundation Level students, the second at Credit Level.

Series: Standard Grade History
Author: Madden, Craig
Publisher: Hodder and Stoughton Educational
Publication Date: 1992
ISBN: 0340532823
Cost: £6.75
Medium: Book
Pupil Audience: Standard Grade

Changing Life in Scotland and Britain 1830–1930

Lucid text includes detailed analysis of statistical tables and legislation. Each chapter is followed by a two-page evaluation exercise, in which pupils are asked questions relating to statistics and selected extracts from source material. Chapters cover population change, living conditions, living and working on the land, coal mining, the railways, technological advances in the last two industries, and parliamentary reform. Illustrated with black and white photos, diagrams and drawings.

Authors: Cameron, Ronald; Henderson, Christine and Robertson, Charles
Publisher: Pulse Publications
Publication Date: 1997
ISBN: 0948766468
Cost: £6.95
Medium: Book
Pupil Audience: Standard Grade

The Crofters

Historical background, list of documents, extracts and facsimiles.

Please see the entry for *Freedom is a Noble Thing* on page 10 for a description of the History at Source series.

Series: History At Source
Publisher: Scottish Record Office
Publication Date: 1993
ISBN: 1870874072
Cost: £3.50
Medium: Primary source booklet
Pupil Audience: Standard Grade/Higher

The Emigrants

Historical background, list of documents, extracts and facsimiles.

Please see the entry for *Freedom is a Noble Thing* on page 10 for a description of the History at Source series.

Series: History At Source
Publisher: Scottish Record Office
Publication Date: 1994
ISBN: 187087403X
Cost: £3.50
Medium: Primary source booklet
Pupil Audience: Standard Grade/Higher

The '45 and After

Historical background, list of documents, extracts and facsimiles.

Please see the entry for *Freedom is a Noble Thing* on page 10 for a description of the History at Source series.

Series: History At Source
Publisher: Scottish Record Office
Publication Date: 1995
ISBN: 187087417X
Cost: £3.50
Medium: Primary source booklet
Pupil Audience: Standard Grade/Higher

The Massacre of Glencoe

Historical background, list of documents, extracts and facsimiles.

Please see the entry for *Freedom is a Noble Thing* on page 10 for a description of the History at Source series.

Series: History At Source
Publisher: Scottish Record Office
Publication Date: 1996
Cost: £3.50
Medium: Primary source booklet
Pupil Audience: Standard Grade/Higher

The Other Georgian Edinburgh

Historical background, list of documents, extracts and facsimiles.

Please see the entry for *Freedom is a Noble Thing* on page 10 for a description of the History at Source series.

Series: History At Source
Publisher: Scottish Record Office
Publication Date: 1993
ISBN: 1870874129
Cost: £3.50
Medium: Primary source booklet
Pupil Audience: Standard Grade/Higher

Poor Relief in Scotland

Historical background, list of documents, extracts and facsimiles.

Please see the entry for *Freedom is a Noble Thing* on page 10 for a description of the History at Source series.

Series: History At Source
Publisher: Scottish Record Office
Publication Date: 1995
ISBN: 1870874188
Cost: £3.50
Medium: Primary source booklet
Pupil Audience: Standard Grade/Higher

The Scots in America

Historical background, list of documents, extracts and facsimiles.

Please see the entry for *Freedom is a Noble Thing* on page 10 for a description of the History at Source series.

Series: History At Source
Publisher: Scottish Record Office
Publication Date: 1994
ISBN: 1870874110
Cost: £3.50
Medium: Primary source booklet
Pupil Audience: Standard Grade/Higher

The Scots in Australia

Historical background, list of documents, extracts and facsimiles.

Please see the entry for *Freedom is a Noble Thing* on page 10 for a description of the History at Source series.

Series: History At Source
Publisher: Scottish Record Office
Publication Date: 1994
ISBN: 1870874099
Cost: £3.50
Medium: Primary source booklet
Pupil Audience: Standard Grade/Higher

The Scots in Canada

Historical background, list of documents, extracts and facsimiles.

Please see the entry for *Freedom is a Noble Thing* on page 10 for a description of the History at Source series.

Series: History At Source
Publisher: Scottish Record Office
Publication Date: 1994
ISBN: 1870874080
Cost: £3.50
Medium: Primary source booklet
Pupil Audience: Standard Grade/Higher

The Scots in New Zealand

Historical background, list of documents, extracts and facsimiles.

Please see the entry for *Freedom is a Noble Thing* on page 10 for a description of the History at Source series.

Series: History At Source
Publisher: Scottish Record Office
Publication Date: 1994
ISBN: 1870874102
Cost: £3.50
Medium: Primary source booklet
Pupil Audience: Standard Grade/Higher

The Victorians

Historical background, list of documents, extracts and facsimiles.

Please see the entry for *Freedom is a Noble Thing* on page 10 for a description of the History at Source series.

Series: History at Source
Publisher: Scottish Record Office
Publication Date: 1993
ISBN: 1870874145
Cost: £3.50
Medium: Primary source booklet
Pupil Audience: Standard Grade/Higher

Fever in Nineteenth Century Glasgow

A loose-leaf collection of source material about the epidemic diseases which were a feature of many nineteenth-century towns in Britain, and about how they affected the history of Glasgow. It includes statistics about epidemics; causes of cholera, typhus and relapsing fever; medical officers of health and the struggle to eradicate infectious diseases.

Publisher: Glasgow City Council: Glasgow City Archives
Publication Date: 1996
Cost: £9.00
Medium: Resource pack
Pupil Audience: Standard Grade but also relevant to other year groups.

Public Health in Nineteenth Century Glasgow

This pack is a loose-leaf collection of source material about the environmental problems which developed in the growing towns of nineteenth-century Britain, and about how these affected the history of Glasgow. It includes descriptions of housing conditions, industrial pollution, water supply and sanitation.

Publisher: Glasgow City Council: Glasgow City Archives
Publication Date: 1996
Cost: £12.00
Medium: Resource pack
Pupil Audience: Standard Grade but also relevant to other year groups.

Scottish Women and the Vote

The pack is a loose-leaf collection of source material on the campaign for women's suffrage in Scotland. (There is an emphasis on sources from the West of Scotland). The sources are grouped with introductory notes under the following headings: Women and Politics in the 19th Century, the Women's Suffrage Movement in the 19th Century, the 'Constitutional' Suffrage Movement, the 'Militant' Suffrage Movement, Mrs Pankhurst in St Andrew's Halls and Scottish Women and the Vote. There is also guidance on further study for pupils and teachers.

Publisher: Glasgow City Council: Glasgow City Archives
Publication Date: 1995
Cost: £13.00
Medium: Resource pack
Pupil Audience: Standard Grade but also relevant to other year groups.

Britain 1850–1979: A Developing Democracy

This book is divided into two sections: The Victorian and Edwardian Context, 1850–1914, and The Twentieth Century Context, 1914–79. Each of these sections evaluates five key issues: 'How and Why did British Society Change?'; 'Towards Democracy?'; 'Winning the Voters' Support'; 'Political Power in Action'; and 'A United Kingdom?' Within this analytical framework the text covers the relevant parts of the syllabus for Section A, Britain 1850–1979 of Option C in Higher History, and includes discussion of Scottish Nationalism and devolution. Illustrated with black and white photographs.

Author: Wood, Sydney
Publisher: Oliver and Boyd
Publication Date: 1992
ISBN: 0050046020
Cost: £9.99
Medium: Book
Pupil Audience: Higher

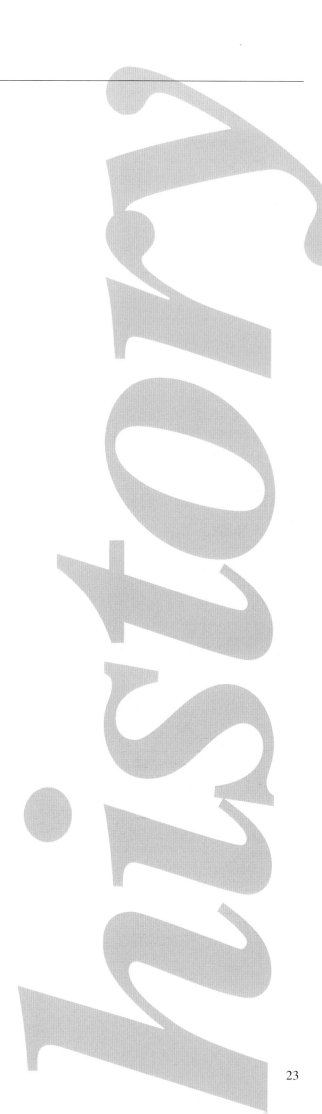

Changing Britain 1850–1979

This book (aimed at Section A, Britain 1850–1979, of Option C in Higher History) contains chapters on all the relevant parts of the syllabus including the Labour movement, the growth of democracy, the Liberal welfare reforms, Scottish Nationalism and devolution. Lucid and readable text belies a generally dry layout. With amendments the book will remain relevant for Higher Still History.

Authors: Morrison, Elliot and Morrison, Donald
Publisher: Pulse Publications
Publication Date: 1992
ISBN: 0948766115
Cost: £7.95
Medium: Book
Pupil Audience: Higher

Fortress Scotland and The Jacobites

Detailed investigation of the hundred years in Scotland between 1650 and 1750 beginning with Cromwell's invasion and ending with the fall of the Jacobite army at Culloden. The text highlights the intensive military activity during this period. Good illustrations.

Authors: Tabraham, Chris and Grove, Doreen
Publisher: Batsford/Historic Scotland
Publication Date: 1995
ISBN: 071347484X
Cost: £15.99
Medium: Book
Pupil Audience: Higher/Certificate of Sixth Year Studies

Industrial Archaeology

This bibliography was compiled to support the Certificate of Sixth Year Studies (CSYS) History field of study on Industrial Archaeology. Although the field of study relates to Britain as a whole, the Scottish dimension receives considerable attention in this publication. In Section 2, 'Sources for Industrial History and Industrial Archaeology', Scottish sources are discussed and described in detail. Also, Section 4 highlights the Scottish dimension while taking account of more general work published in the field.

Series: Curriculum Support Series 16 (iii)
Author: Donnachie, I.
Publisher: Scottish CCC
Publication Date: 1993
ISBN: 185955007X
Cost: £2.00
Medium: Booklet
Pupil Audience: Certificate of Sixth Year Studies

Billy Leaves Home

Black and white A4 activity booklet based on Billy's experiences being evacuated from his home in Partick to Kippen. Well illustrated and includes questions, exercises and discussion and activity sections.

Author: Morrison, Dorothy
Publisher: Northern College
Publication Date: 1977
Cost: £1.00 plus £0.50 p+p
Medium: Book
Pupil Audience: P6–P7

Jock Stein: A Scots Life

A Scots language biography of the great Celtic and Scotland football manager aimed at younger and new readers in Scots. Published in May 1997, this aims to explore the connection between Stein's industrial working class upbringing in Lanarkshire, and his subsequent achievements.

Series: Scots Legends
Author: Telfer, Glenn
Publisher: Argyll Publishing
Publication Date: 1997
ISBN: 1874640130
Cost: £6.99
Medium: Book
Pupil Audience: P6–S2

Scotland and the Second World War

This addition to the Scottie Books series is due for publication in May 1997.

Series: Scottie Books
Authors: McLullich, Helen and Bedborough, Sheena
Publisher: HMSO/National Museums of Scotland
Publication Date: 1997
ISBN: 0114958149
Cost: £4.99
Medium: Book
Pupil Audience: P6–S2

Scotland in World War II

Given the popularity of the topic this is a timely publication covering the home front in Scotland. Chapters include: Blitz on the Clyde, Joining Up, Making Do on the Rations and Women at War. The book also includes previously under-publicised aspects of the War, notably extensive training of commandos in the Highlands. Well illustrated with a glossary and suggested places to visit.

Author: Dargie, Richard
Publisher: Wayland
Publication Date: 1997
ISBN: 0750218746
Cost: £10.99
Medium: Book
Pupil Audience: P6–S2

Scotland 1939

Stimulating montage compilation of archive photographs and short cuttings from Scottish national and local press, covering all aspects of life on the home front. Grouped together under headings: 'Preparing for War', 'Hoping for Peace and Objecting to War', 'International Affairs', 'The Threat from the Air', 'The Impact of War', 'All Working Together', and 'Food and Rationing'. Includes teacher's notes.

Editors: Osborne, Brian and Craig, Robert
Publisher: Scottish Library Association
Publication Date: 1989
ISBN: 0900649690
Cost: £4.50
Medium: Book
Pupil Audience: P6–S2

Scotland 1945

Like its companion, *Scotland 1939*, this is a stimulating combination of photographs, period advertisements and short extracts from national and local newspapers. The material, which has a strong local flavour, is grouped under subject headings: 'Dispatches from the Front and News of the Troops', 'The Home Front', 'Victory At Last', 'Politics', 'Europe', 'Housing' and 'The Planned State'. Includes teacher's notes.

Editors: Osborne, Brian D. and Craig, Robert
Publisher: Scottish Library Association
Publication Date: 1995
ISBN: 0900649933
Cost: £4.99
Medium: Book
Pupil Audience: P6–S2

The Civilian War

Resource pack containing loose-leaf sections on the blackout and the Blitz; women at war; shortages; evacuees and refugees; the war effort; propaganda; food shortages; and the Home Guard. Each section contains fold-out sheets with photographs, period advertisements and printed material, together with an information sheet giving background and pupil questions requiring analysis of the visual material. The pack also includes a sample national registration identity card and ration book, and a teacher's guide.

Authors: Cuthbert, Mary and Morrison, Dorothy
Publisher: Northern College
Publication Date: 1975
Cost: £5.00 plus £0.50 p+p
Medium: Resource pack
Pupil Audience: P6–Standard Grade

Bonnie Fechters: Women in Scotland 1900–1950

This draws on the recollections and life stories of individual witnesses to explore the wider role of women in Scottish society in the first half of the twentieth century. Chapters cover women at work, in politics, in wartime, and in the home. Throughout it draws on the experiences and case histories of a wide range of women, from working mothers to educationalists, suffragettes and inspirational figures like Jenny Lee. Well illustrated with photographs.

Author: Livingstone, Sheila
Publisher: Scottish Library Association
Publication Date: 1994
ISBN: 0900649895
Cost: £4.99
Medium: Book
Pupil Audience: P7–S2, Standard Grade

The First World War

A well produced large format compilation of archive photographs, extracts, facsimiles of documents and other primary source material from Scottish Record Office collections. Contents include sections on The Path of Duty, The Western Front and Dardanelles, The Home Front, News From the Battlefields, Attitudes to the War, and Land, Sea and Air. Includes private letters, maps, orders and reports, together with posters and facsimiles of printed matter. Black and white.

Publisher: Scottish Record Office
Publication Date: 1986
ISBN: 0114933391
Cost: £3.50
Medium: Resource book
Pupil Audience: P7–S2, Standard Grade

Scotland and Britain 1830–1980

Part of the Standard Grade History series, this draws on a wide range of primary and secondary source material (the first part of each chapter being aimed at General and Upper Foundation Level students, the second at Credit Level). Each of the three chronological sections, covering 1830–80, 1880–1939, and the post-war period, includes chapters on people at work, home and health, standards of living, poverty and education, together with variously titled chapters on political developments and popular culture in the respective periods. Illustrated with black and white photographs, drawings, maps and diagrams, and well-provided with statistical data, it also features panels suggesting a range of questions, exercises and activities.

Series: Standard Grade History
Authors: Chalmers, S. A. S. and Cheyne, Larry
Publisher: Hodder and Stoughton Educational
Publication Date: 1992
ISBN: 0340542128
Cost: £6.99
Medium: Book
Pupil Audience: Standard Grade

The Blitz on Clydeside

A loose-leaf collection of source material about the nights of 13 and 14 March 1941 – the worst two nights of bombing in Scotland and the nights when Clydebank was hit. The pack includes an introductory section and two detailed sections, one on Clydebank and the other on one of the most serious of the air-raid incidents in Glasgow.

Publisher: Glasgow City Council: Glasgow City Archives
Publication Date: 1995
Cost: £12.00
Medium: Resource pack
Pupil Audience: Standard Grade but also relevant to other year groups.

Evacuation

A loose-leaf collection of source material about the evacuation of mothers and children from the industrial areas of the West of Scotland. The documents are drawn from both the home areas and the reception areas, and include school records, statistics, oral testimony, official reports and correspondence, newspaper reports and transcripts of parliamentary debates.

Publisher: Glasgow City Council: Glasgow City Archives
Publication Date: 1996
Cost: £12.00
Medium: Resource pack
Pupil Audience: Standard Grade but also relevant to other year groups.

The Women of Royaumont: A Scottish Women's Hospital on the Western Front

The wartime experiences of a group of women who ran a hospital near the trenches during the First World War, largely told through letters and diaries. The book throws light on wartime conditions and the cause of women's suffrage. The text includes illustrations.

Author: Crofton, Eileen
Publisher: Tuckwell Press
Publication Date: 1997
ISBN: 1898410860
Cost: £17.99
Medium: Book
Pupil Audience: Certificate of Sixth Year Studies

Working Lives: Photographs of Workers and their Work in Scotland 1897–1997

Produced for the centenary of the Scottish Trades Union Congress this book contains a wide range of photographs showing people 'who in order to live have had to sell their labour power'. Photographs are collated under chapter headings: Landworkers; Fishing; Fuel and Power; Textiles; Food and Drink; Wood; Stone; Building and Furnishing; Engineering and Metals; Shipbuilding; Printing; Transport; Public Sector; Office-Workers; Domestic Servants; Workers in War; Unemployed; Strikes and Some Other Workers. Some of the photographs are well known, for example, working seaweed into a croft on Skye, but others provide a welcome opportunity to study lesser known scenes including the final photograph of a worker in a lace factory in Darvel in 1926. Useful on its own account, this book is particularly helpful in the search for different primary sources to illustrate course work and examinations.

Author: MacDougall, Ian
Publisher: Scottish Library Association
Publication Date: 1997
ISBN: 0900649976
Cost: £4.99
Medium: Book
Pupil Audience: Not specific to any year group.

A Sense of History: Scotland (P1–P3)

This evaluation pack consists of 15 books, 15 posters and a teacher's guide. The books are titled: *Homes in Scotland, Grandparents in Scotland, Teddy Bears, Birthdays, Our Toys, Children in History, Our Pets, Working Horses, Under the Ground, Shops and Shopping, Lights and Candles, Castles, Playground Games, Food and Traditional Clothes*. The series provides simple texts with copious colour illustrations. Primary sources, for example, pictures, objects and oral reminiscences, are used to encourage pupils to find out for themselves and they are given a vocabulary to discuss the past. The teacher's guide includes separate sections on each topic together with suggestions for follow-up classroom activities, and photocopiable worksheets. The series won the annual Times Educational Supplement (Scotland) award for books supporting the Scottish curriculum.

General Editor: Purkis, Sallie
Publisher: Addison Wesley Longman
Publication Date: 1995
ISBN: 0582249864
Cost: £99.00
Medium: Evaluation pack
Pupil Audience: P1–P3

Touching the Past: Archaeology 5–14

This book grew out of the 'Touching the Past' seminar held in 1995 which brought together archaeologists and teachers to discuss the role of archaeology within Environmental Studies 5–14. It contains a wide variety of ideas concerning the use of archaelogy in schools, with contributions from Historic Scotland's Education Service, Medieval Aberdeen and Glasgow Museums, among others. The book provides a link between the classroom and field studies with Peter Dreghorn's chapter on 'Education in the Middle of Nowhere?' providing useful guidance on how to prepare pupils for a site visit. Preparation includes a simulated dig, reference to site plans and photographs, alongside locating the site on the Ordnance Survey map. The book also includes guidance and information on several museums.

Editors: Curtis, Yule and Curtis, Elizabeth
Publisher: Scottish Children's Press
Publication Date: 1996
ISBN: 1899827633
Cost: £4.95
Medium: Book
Pupil Audience: P1–S2

Scotland's Kings and Queens

This chronological survey is divided into the following chapters: The Making of a Kingdom, 843–1058 AD; Malcolm III; The House of Canmore 1093–1165 and 1165–1290; The House of Bruce, 1306–71; The House of Stewart, 1371–1460; Mary Queen of Scots, 1542–67; James IV, 1567–1603. The clearly written text focuses on the most prominent personalities and events, and the colour layout features a wide range of painted and illuminated portraits, as well as family trees, maps and drawings. Includes a glossary and timeline.

Author: Rasmusen, Barbara Mure
Publisher: Heinemann
Publication Date: 1996
ISBN: 0431078726
Cost: £7.99
Medium: Book
Pupil Audience: P3–P5

Scottish Castles Through History

An illustrated book looking at the role of castles throughout Scotland's history will be published in Spring 1998 (see also Section 2, page 35).

Author: Dargie, Richard
Publisher: Wayland Publishers
ISBN: 0750220562
Cost: £10.99
Medium: Book
Publication Date: March 1998
Pupil Audience: P4-P6

Emigration from Scotland

A well illustrated colour survey divided into four main sections: Emigration in Stuart Times; Emigration in North America; Emigration in Victorian Times; and Famous Scottish Emigrants, which contains short biographies of John Muir, Andrew Carnegie and Alexander Graham Bell. The contents include separate chapters on the emigrants' main countries of destination, together with a concluding Living Links chapter on the Scottish legacy overseas. The layout features colour photographs, maps and illustrations and the clearly written text makes good use of primary evidence, and includes suggested activities for pupils. A teacher's book and evaluation pack for the series is available. The series won the annual Times Educational Supplement (Scotland) award for books supporting the Scottish curriculum.

Please see the entry for 'A Sense of History, Scotland' below for a description of the general series.

Series: A Sense of History, Scotland
Author: Lawson, Douglas
Publisher: Addison Wesley Longman
Publication Date: 1996
ISBN: 0582262259
Cost: £22.50 for pack of 5
Medium: Book
Pupil Audience: P4–P7

A Sense of History: Scotland (P4–P7)

The Sense of History Scotland series provides well-printed, straightforward and interesting texts, with copious colour photographs and illustrations. This evaluation pack comprises four books: *Ancient Scotland, Wars of Independence, The Highland Clearances* and *Emigration from Scotland*. In addition, 12 posters and 12 timelines are included, plus a teacher's guide which contains detailed sections on each of the four titles, providing background and suggesting activities, together with photocopiable 'copymasters'. The series won the annual Times Educational Supplement (Scotland) award for books supporting the Scottish curriculum.

Series: A Sense of History: Scotland
General Editors: Purkis, Sallie and Mason, James
Publisher: Addison Wesley Longman
Publication Date: 1996
ISBN: 058229374X
Cost: £55.00
Medium: Evaluation pack
Pupil Audience: P4–P7

Four Historical Plays

Written in a mixture of Scots and English, and selected for their humour, historical background and sincere yet straightforward language, these plays enable children to imagine everyday life in the past.

Publisher: Scottish Children's Press
Publication Date: Late 1997
Cost: Price to be announced
Medium: Book
Pupil Audience: P5–S2

The Clans

This full colour book provides information on most aspects of clan history and culture. Beginning with 'What is a Clan?' chapters focus on clan names, the Gaelic language, clan chiefs, harpers and pipers, and differences between Border, Lowland and Highland clans. There are also chapters on tartan, the kilt and clan slogans, badges, and plants, as well as clan gatherings and games. The clear text includes a wide range of stimulating questions and activities, and the centrefold forms the 'Cattle-Reiving' game. A list of places to visit is included.

Series: Scottie Books
Author: Jarvie, Gordon
Publisher: HMSO/National Museums of Scotland
Publication Date: 1995
ISBN: 0114953015
Cost: £4.50
Medium: Book
Pupil Audience: P6–S2

Looking at Scottish Art

Although this book focuses on Art, it features several artists and paintings of historical importance. These include Henry Raeburn, Thomas Faed and William McTaggart. The book reproduces Thomas Faed's wonderfully evocative painting 'Last of the Clan', which would make a good introduction to a series of lessons on the Highland Clearances. The book is beautifully illustrated with a wide selection of paintings. It also contains a glossary and a list of galleries and museums to visit.

Authors: McGeoch, Brian and Porch, Steven
Publisher: Wayland/BBC Education Scotland
Publication Date: 1997
ISBN: 0750217499
Cost: £10.99
Medium: Book
Pupil Audience: P6–S2

Travelling Scotland: A Story of Transport

This full colour activity book tells the story of transport in Scotland, with chapters on ancient boats; seaways and rivers; canals, navies and dredgers; speed under sail; the Steam Ship Company; paddling from Edinburgh to Aberdeen; the puffers; the steam railway age; getting around town; the coming of the car and the English aeronauts. Well illustrated throughout, this provides a wide range of suggested activities for pupils, and includes a list of places to visit.

Series: Scottie Books
Author: Morrison, Ian
Publisher: HMSO/National Museums of Scotland
Publication Date: 1994
ISBN: 0114942641
Cost: £3.95
Medium: Book
Pupil Audience: P6–S2

Exploring Scotland's Historic Sites

Includes 21 two-page sections covering a wide range of periods and themes, from early settlers and Celtic people, to the royal house of Stewart, burgh growth, town dwellings, transport and travel, urban development in Victorian times and the twentieth century. Illustrated with maps, photographs and drawings, each section includes a 'Some Sites to Visit' panel.

Author: Farquharson, Elsie
Publisher: Northern College
Publication Date: 1994
ISBN: 1872054056
Cost: £7.50
Medium: Book
Pupil Audience: P6–Standard Grade

Discover Scotland's History

Adapted from the well known series 'History for Young Scots', this book covers life in Scotland from earliest times to the recent restructuring of the regions in 1996. The book has extensive illustrations and would be relevant for both the classroom and the library.

Author: Cameron, A. D.
Publisher: Scottish Children's Press
Year of Publication: 1996
ISBN: 1898218765
Cost: £9.95
Medium: Book
Pupil Audience: P7–S2

Origins: The History of Emigration from Scotland

Well illustrated large format history that provides narrative though themed chapters on the plantation of Ulster; changes in the Highlands (early emigration to America); the Industrial Revolution (including skilled immigrants to America); the Highland Clearances (the Highland and Islands Emigration Society, and emigration to Australia); Scots throughout the Empire (New Zealand and South Africa); and the Scots abroad, which examines the Scottish cultural legacy overseas.

Author: Hirst, Mike
Publisher: Franklin Watts
Publication Date: 1997
ISBN: 0749625813
Cost: £10.99
Medium: Book
Pupil Audience: P7–S2

Scottish Life 1750 to Recent Times

This book utilises a combination of visual, source and documentary material, together with activity panels containing questions and exercises. The three sections, Economic Change, Nineteenth-century Life and The Twentieth Century, include chapters on farming, mining, manufacturing industry, and different forms of transport, as well as education, health and most aspects of urban and rural life. There are also separate chapters on the growth of Glasgow and Edinburgh, the decline of crofting, and growth of tourism in the Highlands.

Author: Wood, Sydney
Publisher: Stanley Thornes (Publishers) Ltd
Publication Date: 1995
ISBN: 0748720855
Cost: £5.99
Medium: Book
Pupil Audience: P7–S2

Clyde Shipbuilding

A loose-leaf collection of source material on the history of Clyde shipbuilding since around 1880. It comprises documentary extracts, statistics and some photographs. The sources are grouped under the following headings: The Heyday of Clyde Shipbuilding 1880–1914, The First World War, The 1920s and 1930s, The Second World War, The Post-War Years, The Crisis Years and Post 1960.

Publisher: Glasgow City Council: Glasgow City Archives
Publication Date: 1995
Cost: £15.00
Medium: Resource pack
Pupil Audience: Standard Grade but also relevant to other year groups.

'A Happy and Golden Tyme': Education in Scotland Since the Fourteenth Century

Historical background, list of documents, extracts and facsimiles.

Please see the entry for *Freedom is a Noble Thing* on page 10 for a description of the History at Source series.

Series: History at Source.
Publisher: Scottish Record Office
Publication Date: 1994
ISBN: 1870874153
Cost: £3.50
Medium: Primary source booklet
Pupil Audience: Standard Grade/Higher

Exhibition Texts

Exhibition Texts combine notes on the historical background to the chosen theme with a descriptive list of relevant documents. Stapled A4 booklets, they generally include photocopies of manuscripts and illustrated material, together with short extracts from primary sources. Titles include: *The Queen and the Scots: Life in 16th-century Scotland; The North-American Indians: 18th and 19th Centuries; The Scottish Fishing Industry: 18th and 19th Centuries; Scotland and France: To celebrate the 700th anniversary of the Auld Alliance; Friends of Liberty: Scotland and the French Revolution; Feast to Festival: History of Entertainment, Medieval to Modern; Hatches, Matches and Despatches: Rites of Passage, 16–19th Centuries.*

Publisher: Scottish Record Office
Cost: £3.25
Medium: A4 booklets
Pupil Audience: Standard Grade/Higher

The Peoples of Scotland

Historical background, list of documents, extracts and facsimiles.

Please see the entry for *Freedom is a Noble Thing* on page 10 for a description of the History at Source series.

Series: History At Source
Publisher: Scottish Record Office
Publication Date: 1993
ISBN: 1870874137
Cost: £3.50
Medium: Primary source booklet
Pupil Audience: Standard Grade/Higher

Clanship, Commerce and the House of Stuart, 1603–1788

An examination of clanship that attributes the system's decline to the abandonment of personal obligations by the clan elites, rather than to regulation or central government repression. Of possible use for the Certificate of Sixth Year Studies.

Author: MacInnes, Allan I.
Publisher: Tuckwell Press
Publication Date: 1996
ISBN: 1898410240
Cost: £16.99
Medium: Book
Pupil Audience: Certificate of Sixth Year Studies

Atlas of Scottish History to 1707

This atlas replaces the *Historical Atlas of Scotland c.400 – c.1600* which was published in 1975 by the Scottish Medievalists and which went out of print some years ago. The present atlas has been almost fifteen years in the making. It contains not only maps, but also diagrams, plans, charts and tables covering the history of Scotland from the earliest times up to 1707, along with explanatory texts where these are necessary. The table of contents shows the range of matters covered in the atlas. Naturally, most of the atlas is concerned with the lands which were later to form the kingdom of Scotland, but other maps deal with Scotland's contact with other countries – chiefly with the nearest neighbour, England, but also with Ireland, several small parts of Europe, a small part of Asia and the Americas. As with the previous atlas, this new enlarged atlas is designed not only for students but also for anyone who has an interest in the development of Scotland.

Authors: McNeill, Peter G. B. and MacQueen, Hector
Publisher: The Scottish Medievalists and Department of Geography, University of Edinburgh
Publication Date: 1996
ISBN: 0950390410
Cost: £30
Medium: Book
Pupil Audience: Not specific to any year group

Section 2

Audio-Visual Materials

The audio-visual materials in this section are provided by the BBC and Channel 4. Resources are listed under the general headings of:

- Primary, to be broadcast in 1997–8
- Primary, broadcast in previous years
- Secondary, to be broadcast in 1997–8
- Secondary, broadcast in previous years.

Within these categories, television and radio programmes are listed in ascending order according to pupil year groups. Where support materials are available, this is indicated within the entry.

For further information regarding BBC Education programmes contact: John Russell, Senior Education Officer, BBC Scotland, Room 306, Broadcasting House, 5 Queen Street, Edinburgh EH2 1JF (Tel: 0131 248 4261).

Further details of Channel 4 programmes and supporting materials can be found in *Channel 4 Television and Resources for Primary and Secondary Schools 1997–98*, obtainable from: Channel 4 Schools, P.O. Box 100, Warwick, CV34 6T2.

The address in Scotland is: Anne Fleck, Education Officer, Channel 4 Schools, 74 Victoria Crescent Road, Dowanhill, Glasgow G12 9JL.

People in The Past

Five radio programmes in the series 'Scottish Resources: 7–9', Autumn 1997. Events from the lives of five famous Scots: Donald McBean; Flora McDonald; Lady Catherine Douglas; Willie Douglas; Mary Queen of Scots; and Lord Thomas Cochrane.

Teacher/pupil notes are available to purchase from BBC Education Scotland, details: 0131 248 4261.

Broadcaster: Radio 3 FM NightTime
Broadcast Date: Autumn 1997
Medium: Radio
Pupil Audience: P3–P5

The Romans

Three radio programmes in the series 'Scottish Resources: 7–9', Spring 1998. The programmes explore everything from footwear to food in an adventure with the Celts.

Teacher/pupil notes and audio cassettes are available to purchase from BBC Education Scotland, details: 0131 248 4261.

'Caledonians and Romans' (BBC Education Scotland), a poster pack with pupil worksheets for use at Middle Stages, is available from BBC Education Scotland, details: 0131 248 4261.

The Romans in Scotland (BBC Education/Wayland), an illustrated reference book giving an account of military and social features of the Roman period in Scotland, will be published in Spring 1998.

Broadcaster: Radio 3 FM NightTime
Broadcast Date: Spring 1998
Medium: Radio/audio cassettes
Pupil Audience: P3–P5

The Vikings in Scotland

Five television programmes in the series 'See You See Me'. Through a mixture of drama and documentary sequences we follow major events and daily life in the time of the Vikings in Scotland.

Teacher/pupil notes and an illustrated book, *The Vikings in Scotland*, are available to purchase from BBC Education Scotland, details: 0131 248 4261. (See also Section 1, page 7.)

Broadcaster: BBC2
Broadcast Date: Spring 1998
Medium: Television
Pupil Audience: P3–P5

Na Lochlannaich An Alba

Five television programmes in the Gaelic middle stages series 'Tuig!' A mixture of drama and documentary sequences on life in the time of the Vikings in Scotland.

Teacher/pupil notes and an illustrated book, *The Vikings in Scotland*, are available to purchase from BBC Education Scotland, details: 0131 248 4261 (see also Section 1, page 7).

Broadcaster: BBC2
Broadcast Date: Spring 1998
Medium: Television
Pupil Audience: P3–P5

Na Lochlannaich

Four radio programmes in the Gaelic middle stages series 'Eadar Eisdeachd'. Two children travel back in time and join a Viking raid.

Teacher/pupil notes, audio cassettes and an illustrated book, *The Vikings in Scotland*, are available to purchase from BBC Education Scotland, details: 0131 248 4261 (see also Section 1, page 7).

Broadcaster: Radio 3 FM NightTime
Broadcast Date: Autumn 1997
Medium: Radio/audio cassettes
Pupil Audience: P3–P5

Calum Cille

Three radio programmes in the Gaelic middle stages series 'Eadar Eisdeachd'. Some dramatic episodes in Columba's life.

Teacher/pupil notes and audio cassettes are available to purchase from BBC Education Scotland, details: 0131 248 4261.

Broadcaster: Radio 3 FM NightTime
Broadcast Date: Autumn 1997
Medium: Radio/audio cassettes
Pupil Audience: P3–P5

Chuck Wallace's Middle Age Spread

A series of five television programmes on Scotland in the time of Wallace and Bruce. Please see page 8 for details of the teacher's guide to accompany the series.

Broadcaster: Channel 4
Broadcast Date: May/June 1998
Medium: Television
Pupil Audience: P5–P7

The Jacobites

A series of five television programmes made to coincide with the 250th anniversary of the Jacobite Rebellion of 1745 and intended as a cross-curricular resource for children aged 9–12. A teacher's guide to accompany the series is available (see page 17 for details). The series is due to be broadcast again in the Autumn of 1998, probably for the last time, with transmission of the first programme currently scheduled for 24 September 1998. Also available on video from Channel 4 Schools.

Broadcaster: Channel 4
Broadcast Date: September/October 1998
Medium: Television/video
Pupil Audience: P5–S1

Robert Burns: Alive and Kicking

This series of five television programmes is aimed at pupils aged 10–12 and not only illustrates the main events of Burns' life, but also seeks to show how and why some of his most important and influential poems were written. A teacher's guide to accompany the series is available (see page 18 for details). The series is due to be broadcast in Autumn 1997, with the transmission of the first programme currently scheduled for 26 September. It is also available on five 50-minute videos from Channel 4 Schools.

Broadcaster: Channel 4
Broadcast Date: September/October 1997
Medium: Television/video
Pupil Audience: P6–S2

Bruce's Scotland

Five television programmes in the series 'Around Scotland', Autumn 1997. This drama/documentary is set after the Battle of Methven in 1306. A Scottish soldier on the run from the English forces seeks help from the shepherd Thomas Galloway and his family.

Teacher/pupil notes are available to purchase from BBC Education Scotland, details: 0131 248 4261.

Bruce's Scotland (BBC Education Scotland/Wayland Publishers Ltd), a fully illustrated pupil reference book, tells how Bruce and his supporters overcame the power of England to re-establish Scottish independence. Available to purchase from BBC Education Scotland: 0131 248 4261, or from Wayland (see Section 1, page 8).

Broadcaster: BBC 2
Broadcast Date: Autumn 1997
Medium: Television
Pupil Audience: P6–S2

Wallace's Scotland

Five radio programmes in the series 'Scottish Resources: 10–12', Autumn 1997. The programmes commemorate the 700th anniversary of the Battle of Stirling Bridge (11 September 1297). Full drama captures the atmosphere of a family torn by the upheavals of war.

Teacher/pupil notes and audio cassettes are available to purchase from BBC Education Scotland, details: 0131 248 4261.

Broadcaster: Radio 3 FM NightTime
Broadcast Date: Autumn 1997
Medium: Radio/audio cassettes
Pupil Audience: P6–S2

Journey to Iona

One television programme in the series 'Around Scotland'. To mark the 1400th anniversary of his death, this programme invites pupils on a personal search through St Columba's world of journeys, buildings, symbols and celebrations.

Teacher/pupil notes are available to purchase from BBC Education Scotland, details: 0131 248 4261.

Broadcaster: BBC2
Broadcast Date: Autumn 1997
Medium: Television
Pupil Audience: P6–S2

Sounds of the '80s

Five radio programmes in the series 'Scottish Resources: 10–12'. Lifestyle, food, fashion and political change in the era of Mrs Thatcher.

Teacher/pupil notes are available to purchase from BBC Education Scotland, details: 0131 248 4261.

Broadcaster: Radio 3 FM NightTime
Broadcast Date: Autumn 1997
Medium: Radio
Pupil Audience: P6–S2

In the Past

Three television programmes in the series 'What? Where? When? Why?' looking at aspects of Edwardian life: in the kitchen; keeping clean; toys and games.

Broadcaster: BBC
Broadcast Date: Autumn 1996
Medium: Video
Pupil Audience: P2–P3

Castles

Five radio programmes in the series 'Scottish Resources 7–9', in which five Scottish castles are examined through the eyes of a character from their history. Audio cassettes of these programmes are available to purchase from BBC Education Scotland, details: 0131 248 4261.

An illustrated book, *Scottish Castles Through History* (BBC Education/Wayland Publishers) looking at the role of castles throughout Scotland's history, will be published in Spring 1998 (see Section 1, page 27).

Broadcaster: BBC
Broadcast Date: Autumn 1996
Medium: Audio cassettes
Pupil Audience: P3–P5

The 1960s

Five television programmes in the series 'See You See Me'. Key features of the decade – entertainment, school life, shops and money, transport and home life.

Broadcaster: BBC
Broadcast Date: Autumn 1995
Medium: Video
Pupil Audience: P3–P5

Rock'n'Roll Perils

Three radio programmes in the series 'Scottish Resources 7–9'. Drama/role-play stimulus – it is 1965 and The Fabulous Four have been kidnapped.

Broadcaster: BBC
Broadcast Date: Spring 1996
Medium: Audio cassettes
Pupil Audience: P3–P5

The Romans in Scotland

Five television drama/documentary programmes in the series 'See You See Me'. Maeve, a young Caledonian, is captured and enslaved at a Roman camp.

A poster pack, 'Caledonians and Romans', including pupil worksheets for use at Middle Stages is available from BBC Education Scotland, details: 0131 248 4261.

The Romans in Scotland (BBC Education Scotland/Wayland Publishers), an illustrated book giving an account of military and social features of the Roman period in Scotland, will be published in Spring 1998 (see Section 1, page 4).

Broadcaster: BBC
Broadcast Date: Autumn 1996
Medium: Video
Pupil Audience: P3–P5

Beyond the Green Wall

Five radio programmes in the series 'Scottish Resources 10–12'. A full drama set around the Antonine Wall at the time of the Romans in Scotland.

A poster pack, 'Caledonians and Romans', including pupil worksheets for use at Middle Stages is available from BBC Education Scotland, details: 0131 248 4261.

The Romans in Scotland (BBC Education Scotland/Wayland Publishers), an illustrated book giving an account of military and social features of the Roman period in Scotland, will be published in Spring 1998 (see Section 1, page 4).

Broadcaster: BBC
Broadcast Date: Spring 1991
Medium: Audio cassettes
Pupil Audience: P3–P5

People in the Past

Five radio programmes in the series 'Scottish Resources 7–9', looking at significant figures from Scottish History: Sgathach, Calgacus, St Columba, The Maid of Norway, Robert the Bruce.

Audio cassettes of these programmes are available to purchase from BBC Education Scotland, details: 0131 248 4261.

Broadcaster: BBC
Broadcast Date: Autumn 1996
Medium: Audio cassettes
Pupil Audience: P3–P5

The Clearances

Four television programmes in the series 'Around Scotland'. A drama/documentary focusing on the background to and events of the Highland Clearances.

An illustrated book, *The Highland Clearances* (see page 17), and software, *The Clearances* (see page 43), are available to purchase from BBC Education Scotland, details: 0131 248 4261.

Broadcaster: BBC
Broadcast Date: Autumn 1993
Medium: Video
Pupil Audience: P6–S2

Fuadaichean

A Gaelic version of *The Clearances* (see entry above) in the series 'Mu Chuairt Alba'.

Broadcaster: BBC
Broadcast Date: Spring 1993
Medium: Video
Pupil Audience: P6–S2

The Desperate Journey

Five radio programmes in the series 'Scottish Resources 10–12', Autumn 1995. A five-part full drama adaptation of Kathleen Fidler's novel.

An illustrated book, *The Highland Clearances* (see page 17), and software, *The Clearances* (see page 43), are available to purchase from BBC Education Scotland, details: 0131 248 4261.

Broadcaster: BBC
Broadcast Date: Autumn 1995
Medium: Audio cassettes
Pupil Audience: P6–S2

Driven West

Five radio programmes in the series 'Scottish Resources 10–12'. A five-part drama focuses on a Highland family forced to emigrate to America and deals with the clash of cultures between whites and native Americans.

An illustrated book, *The Highland Clearances* (see page 17), and software, *The Clearances* (see page 43), are available to purchase from BBC Education Scotland, details: 0131 248 4261.

Broadcaster: BBC
Broadcast Date: Autumn 1995
Medium: Audio cassettes
Pupil Audience: P6–S2

The Year of the Prince

Five television programmes in the series 'Around Scotland'. A drama/documentary focusing on the background to the 1745 Jacobite Rising and the effects of the Battle of Culloden on a small Highland community.

An illustrated book (*The Jacobites*, see page 17), wallchart (full colour, including time line and pupil activity pack) and software (*Jacobites – The Lost Succession*, see page 43 are available to purchase from BBC Education Scotland, details: 0131 248 4261.

Broadcaster: BBC
Broadcast Date: Spring 1995
Medium: Video
Pupil Audience: P6–S2

Bliadhna A' Phrionnsa

A Gaelic version of *The Year of the Prince* (see entry above) in the series 'Mu Chuairt Alba'.

Broadcaster: BBC
Broadcast Date: Spring 1995
Medium: Video
Pupil Audience: P6–S2

Scottish

A Parcel of Rogues

Five radio programmes in the series 'Scottish Resources 10–12'. A drama serial, set in 1715, follows the adventures of two children caught up in the Jacobite Rising.

An illustrated book (*The Jacobites*, see page 17), wallchart (full colour, including time line and pupil activity pack) and software (*Jacobites – The Lost Succession*, see page 43) are available to purchase from BBC Education Scotland, details: 0131 248 4261.

Broadcaster: BBC
Broadcast Date: Spring 1995
Medium: Audio cassettes
Pupil Audience: P6–S2

Change and Liberty

Five television programmes in the series 'Around Scotland'. The drama/documentary programmes explore the political and economic movements in late eighteenth-century Scotland.

Broadcaster: BBC
Broadcast Date: Autumn 1996
Medium: Video
Pupil Audience: P6–S2

The Story and the Song: Burns

Five radio programmes in the series 'Scottish Resources 10–12'. Specially written stories woven around five of Burns' songs describe key stages of the poet's life.

Audio cassettes of these programmes are available to purchase from BBC Education Scotland, details: 0131 248 4261.

A book (*Scotland in the Time of Burns*, see page 16 and wallchart ('A Man's A Man For A' That', including pupil activities pack) are available to purchase from BBC Education Scotland, details: 0131 248 4261.

Broadcaster: BBC
Broadcast Date: Autumn 1996
Medium: Audio cassettes
Pupil Audience: P6–S2

Children of Coal and Iron

Five television programmes in the series 'Around Scotland'. Drama/documentary focusing on conditions and conflicts in Scottish coal mines of the nineteenth century.

A book (*Children of Coal and Iron*, see page 18) and full colour poster depicting Lanarkshire in 1840 are available to purchase from BBC Education Scotland (details: 0131 248 4261) or from Wayland Publishers Ltd.

Broadcaster: BBC
Broadcast Date: Autumn 1995
Medium: Video
Pupil Audience: P6–S2

People in the Past

Five radio programmes in the series 'Scottish Resources 10–12'. Set in the 1840s at a time of change in farming, transport and industry.

Broadcaster: BBC
Broadcast Date: Spring 1996
Medium: Audio cassettes
Pupil Audience: P6–S2

The Seventies

Four radio programmes in the series 'Scottish Resources 10–12': old wars, new friendships, the oil crisis and terror in Europe, new movements, Punk and Mrs Thatcher.

Audio cassettes of these programmes are available to purchase from BBC Education Scotland, details: 0131 248 4261.

Broadcaster: BBC
Broadcast Date: Summer 1997
Medium: Audio cassettes
Pupil Audience: P6–S2

History

Act of Union

Five television programmes in the series 'Around Scotland'. This drama/documentary unit deals with the crisis in Scotland in November 1706 when the Scottish Estates (Parliament) prepared to debate the proposals for the Act of Union.

An illustrated book (*The Union* of 1707, see page 18), wallchart (including activity pack) and software (*1707: The Lost Parliament*, see page 43) are available to purchase from BBC Education Scotland, details: 0131 248 4261.

Broadcaster: BBC
Broadcast Date: Spring 1996
Medium: Video
Pupil Audience: P6–S2

Once a Viking

Three radio programmes in the series 'Scottish Resources 7–9'. The raiding and warfare traditions of the Vikings are contrasted with the peaceable activities of the monks.

Audio cassettes of these programmes are available to purchase from BBC Education Scotland, details: 0131 248 4261.

Broadcaster: BBC
Broadcast Date: Spring 1997
Medium: Audio cassettes
Pupil Audience: P6–S2

Standard Grade History

One radio programme on the development of the Welfare State since World War 2, with particular focus on Scotland.

Broadcaster: BBC
Broadcast Date: Spring 1998
Medium: Radio

Higher History

Two radio programmes looking at Appeasement and the Road to War in World War 2.

Broadcaster: BBC
Broadcast Date: Spring 1998
Medium: Radio

Standard Grade History
The Highland Clearances 1
The Highland Clearances 2
Power to the People?
Have Standards Fallen?
The 51st State?

Broadcaster: BBC
Broadcast Date: Autumn 1994
Medium: Television

Standard Grade History
Vote! Strike! (1832 Reform Act and the Chartists Movement)
1918 – Votes for All? (The Scottish Suffrage Movement)
The Labour Party in Scotland (Election 1923)
News from the Russian Front (1917 and 1924)
News from the Russian Front (1929 and 1936)

Broadcaster: BBC
Broadcast Date: Autumn 1992
Medium: Radio

Standard Grade History
Power to the People?
Best Days of Your Life?
The 51st State?
The Permissive Society?
Does the Media Matter?

Broadcaster: BBC
Broadcast Date: Spring 1992
Medium: Television

Standard Grade History
More Mouths to Feed
Made in Scotland
Private Filth and Public Health
Out of Work and Off to School
Bumpy Roads and Boneshakers
Rivals on the Road
Away from It All
Prisons on the Road
Raves from the Grave
Mouldy Oldies

Broadcaster: BBC
Broadcast Date: Spring 1992
Medium: Radio

Standard Grade History
The Highland Clearances (two programmes)
20th Century: Living Through War: Scotland 1939–46
20th Century: Technology and the Scottish People: Roads, Power and Ships 1920s–1960s
20th Century: Scotland's Women, Life and Work, 1930s–1940s.

Broadcaster: BBC
Broadcast Date: Spring 1991
Medium: Television

Standard Grade History
Changing Life in Scotland and Britain: Autobiography of a Working Man (1820s and 1830s), Wheels and Power (late eighteenth century), Politics and People (1832; 1840s–1850).

People and Power: Germany 1918–39: Democracy and Dictatorship, Resistance and Revolution.

Broadcaster: BBC
Broadcast Date: Spring 1991
Medium: Radio

Higher Grade History (Revised)
Britain 1850s–1979: SNP and Devolution 1, SNP and Devolution 2, Women's Suffrage 1850–1918.

Patterns of Migration 1830–1930: Irish Migration to Scotland.

Ireland: A Divided Identity (1) 1900–1916, A Divided Identity (2) 1916–1923.

Broadcaster: BBC
Broadcast Date: Summer 1997
Medium: Radio

Information Technology

The Internet contains a very wide range of resources applicable to Scottish history. However, search engines tend to produce an enormous number of matches (over 100,000 matches to 'Scottish history' were found using Web Crawler) many of which may be of limited relevance to schools. It is better to focus on specific topics, for example, to search for 'William Wallace', or to specify an URL, such as the Celtic and Saxon Homepage at http://www/primenet.com/~lconley/bookmarks.html.

The Scottish Council for Educational Technology (SCET) supports the use of information technology in schools. In 1993 SCET published *Software Evaluations*, which evaluated computer programs applicable to the 5–14 development programme, including Environmental Studies 5–14. Listed below are further details of computer programs which support the teaching of Scottish history.

The Clearances

This computer program contains a database taken from the emigrant passenger lists of HMS Hercules which sailed from Scotland to Australia in 1852–3. The database allows searches for information on the passengers. The program also contains background information on the voyage and passengers, and is supported by teacher's notes. The program also relates to Standard Grade History, Unit 1 Contexts A and B.

Authors: Teacher's notes compiled by Greenwood, Betty and O'Hara, Moira
Publisher: BBC Scotland
Publication Date: 1993
ISBN: 1850692602
Cost: £27.00
Medium: Information technology resource pack containing computer software (Apple MacIntosh) and teacher's notes. Links to the BBC Wayland Book *The Highland Clearances* (see page 17).
Pupil Audience: P4–S2

Desperate Journey

This information technology resource examines the experience of a Highland family during the Clearances. It traces events in Sutherland and the subsequent migration of people within Scotland and emigration to Canada. The pack links with Kathleen Fidler's novel, *The Desperate Journey*, published by Canongate in 1984 (ISBN: 08622410568, price: £1.95).

Authors: Rendell, Fred; Watterson, Patricia, and Fidler, Kathleen
Publisher: University of Strathclyde/Jordanhill College
Publication Date: 1985
ISBN: 1850980438
Cost: £40.00
Medium: Information technology resource pack containing computer software (BBC), teacher's notes and pupil activities.
Pupil Audience: P6–P7

Jacobites: The Lost Succession

This Hypercard based software examines the rival claims to the thrones of Scotland and England. It includes an interactive family tree from James VI and I to the Georges. Sections on the different fighting men available to the Pretender and the Hanoverians, and their weapons, lead to a full understanding of the tactics and battle plans for Culloden.

Authors: Rendell, F.W.; Muir, D.; Pool, T. and Frame, R.
Publisher: University of Strathclyde/BBC Scotland
Publication Date: 1995
ISBN: 1850985464
Cost: £30.20
Medium: Computer software for Apple MacIntosh and Archimedes. Links with the BBC 'Around Scotland' series on the Jacobites (see page 36).
Pupil Audience: P6–S2

1707: The Lost Parliament

This software explores the theme of the 1707 Act of Union, using ideas and storylines provided by Fred Rendell and Arnold Bell. The historical context is developed, from Henry VII marrying his daughter to the King of Scotland to the rise and fall of the Jacobites, and includes Scotland's disastrous venture into international colonisation and trade at Darien. The causes and results of the Union are also discussed.

Authors: Rendell, F.W.; Bell, A.; Muir, D.; Pool, T. and Frame, R.
Publisher: University of Strathclyde/BBC Scotland
Publication Date: 1996
ISBN: 185098557X
Cost: £37.00
Medium: Computer software for Apple MacIntosh. Links with the BBC 'Around Scotland' series on the Act of Union (see page 38).
Pupil Audience: P6–S2

The Bowbridge Pack

The Bowbridge Pack is based on a Register of Accidents kept by Bowbridge Jute Works in Dundee in 1896–7. It includes a datafile of accidents for both years, together with supporting documentation. The study book and tasks help pupils explore the datafile.

Authors: Flavell, Julie, et al.
Publisher: SCET
Year of Publication: 1992
Cost: £24.99
Medium: Information technology resource pack containing computer software (Archimedes, MacIntosh and BBC), teacher's notes, study book and tasks.
Pupil Audience: Standard Grade

Squatters and Saints

This multi-media production examines emigration from Scotland to Australia in the nineteenth century. Topics include Highland emigration, passages, the gold rush, squatters and explorers. Information is presented in text, photographs and animation. The text includes a wide range of primary sources, for example the diaries of emigrants. The program could be used in whole or in parts. Although the language is relatively sophisticated, the program itself is easy to use.

Author: Clyde, Robert
Publisher: Dunedin Multi-Media Ltd
Publication Date: 1996
Cost: £28.99
Medium: CD ROM for Apple MacIntosh and Windows.
Pupil Audience: Standard Grade, Higher and Certificate of Sixth Year Studies.

Clyde Shipbuilding

This CD-ROM contains 186 photographs of Clyde-built ships and of the building methods used in the shipyards since the late nineteenth century. The photographs can be searched by using the information on each image. Each photograph can be printed out for use in the classroom.

Publisher: Glasgow City Council: Glasgow City Archives
Publication Date: 1996
Cost: £10.00
Medium: CD-ROM for Apple MacIntosh and Windows.
Pupil Audience: P6–Higher

Moving House
Glasgow: A Tale of Two Cities
Tiree: Famine and Clearance

These computer programs combine a range of primary and secondary sources, including census databases, photographs, film and dramatic reconstruction, to examine the history of Glasgow and Tiree in the nineteenth and twentieth century. Teacher's notes relate the program to the relevant national syllabus. Each program contains pupil exercises and associated tasks such as model making and suggested locations for field studies.

Moving House
Authors: Hillis, Peter and Calderhead, Drew
Publisher: University of Strathclyde
Publication Date: 1993
Cost: £10.00
Media: Information technology resource pack containing computer software (Apple MacIntosh), teacher's notes and pupil activities.
Pupil Audience: P6–Higher

Glasgow: A Tale of Two Cities
Authors: Hillis, Peter and Calderhead, Drew
Publisher: University of Strathclyde
Publication Date: 1994
Cost: £25.00
Media: Information technology resource pack containing computer software (Apple MacIntosh), teacher's notes and pupil activities.
Pupil Audience: P6–Higher

Tiree: Famine and Clearance
Authors: Hillis, Peter and Calderhead, Drew
Publisher: University of Strathclyde
Publication Date: 1995
Cost: £15.00
Media: Information technology resource packs containing computer software (Apple MacIntosh), teacher's notes and pupil activities.
Pupil Audience: P6–Higher

The Scottish People: A Social and Economic History 1840-1940 (CD-ROM)

This multi-media Scottish history CD-ROM for schools contain information on economic, social and cultural developments in Scotland over the period 1840-1940. It offers pupils and their teachers an exploratory resource that encourages active participation in the learning process. It charts the development and decline of industralisation over the period using text, data-sets, film and audio. The narrative of the resource seeks to develop and understanding of economic growth through scientific and technological change, together with the concomitant effects on people's lives. Multi-media essays provide the foundation for class work with key words linking to supporting information, images and data acquired from sources such as the National Museums of Scotland and the Scottish Film Library.

Publisher: Scottish CCC
Publication Date: 1997
Cost: £10.75
Medium: CD-ROM for Apple MacIntosh and PC
Pupil Audience: P6–S5

The Companion to Scottish History

This multi-media CD-ROM aims to provide instant facts on Scottish history. From an alphabetical index pupils can find information on themes ranging from the Aberdeenshire Canal to the Young Pretender. Most of the information is presented as text but there are pictures, animation and video. The CD-ROM serves as an encyclopedia and used selectively would help provide useful information, although some of the language is quite sophisticated.

Authors: Donnachie, Ian and Hewitt, George
Editor: Clyde, Robert
Publisher: Dunedin Multi-Media
Publication Date: 1996
Cost: £34.99
Medium: CD-ROM for Apple MacIntosh and Windows.
Pupil Audience: Standard Grade, Higher, Certificate of Sixth Year Studies.

The History of the Highland Clans

This multi-media CD-ROM analyses the history of the clans through the use of essays, maps, pictures, music, animation and video. The essays trace the evolution of the clans and include individual essays on ancient peoples, the MacDonald Lordship of the Isles and Gaelic literature. The CD-ROM is aimed at the general reader, libraries, schools and those interested in Highland history. However, the language level makes the essays difficult for many pupils.

Author: Clyde, Robert with contributions from Mairianna Birkeland
Publisher: Dunedin Multi-Media
Publication Date: 1996
Cost: £28.99
Medium: CD-ROM for Apple MacIntosh and Windows.
Pupil Audience: Standard Grade, Higher, Certificate of Sixth Year Studies.

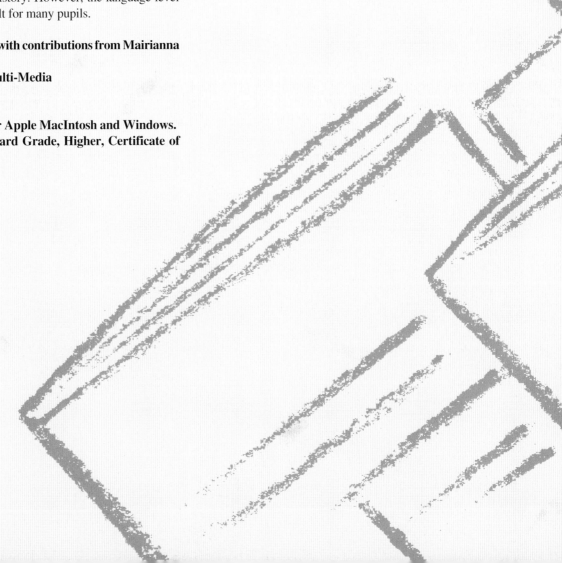

Section 4

Developing Historical Skills in the Context of Standard Grade and Higher History

History Standard Grade Studymate

This book concentrates on developing pupil skills in key areas of Standard Grade, namely knowledge and understanding, evaluating and investigating. For each Standard Grade unit and context, sources and questions guide pupils in the type of answers required for the external examination. A very wide range of sources is quoted, making the book a valuable resource throughout the course and for revision. This book requires alteration to take into account the changes to investigating from 1999.

Author: Johnstone, Muir
Publisher: Hamilton Publishing
Publication Date: Second edition 1995
ISBN: 0946164185
Cost: £8.95
Medium: Book
Pupil Audience: Standard Grade

Passing Higher History

This book guides Higher students through the skills necessary to pass Higher History with reference to Paper 1 essays, the special topic and extended essays. Essay guides are supported by extensive sources and model plans and essays. A very useful resource for continuous use throughout the course and for revision purposes.

Author: Matheson, Ian
Publisher: Hodder and Stoughton
Publication Date: 1996
ISBN: 0340655550
Cost: £6.25
Medium: Book
Pupil Audience: Higher

Revised Higher Resource Pack

Resource pack of factual, supportive detail covering all course options.

Publisher: Scottish Borders Council
Cost: On request. Contact: Mrs Rosemary Milne, Education Department, Scottish Borders Council, Newtown St Boswells TD6 0SA (Tel: 01835 824000; Fax: 01835 822145).
Medium: Resource pack
Pupil Audience: Higher

Section 5

Field Studies

Scotland has a wealth of historical sites suitable for field studies. These range from the remains of Highland townships to organised locations such as Auchindrain, Inveraray Jail, Kingussie Folk Museum, Discovery Point, museums and libraries. The organisations listed below provide resources to support field studies.

SCOTTISH MUSEUMS COUNCIL

The Scottish Museums Council through the Museum Education Initiative provides support for school visits to museums (for example, the publication *Networking in Ross and Cromarty* provides guidance on how museums in Ross and Cromarty can support the curriculum with specific reference to the 5–14 Development Programme). The address for the Scottish Museums Council is:

County House, 20/22 Torphichen Street, Edinburgh EH3 8JB
Tel: 0131 229 7465.

SCOTTISH LIBRARY ASSOCIATION

The Scottish Library Association, Scottish Centre for Information and Library Services provides guidance and publishes books on specific topics (please see Section 1 for details of these books). The address for the Scottish Library Association is:

1 John Street, Hamilton ML3 7EU
Tel: 01698 458888.

NATIONAL MUSEUMS OF SCOTLAND

The National Museums of Scotland provides the following publication to support visits to the Scottish Agricultural Museum.

Scottish Agricultural Museum: A Guide for Teachers

Guidance on preparing a class for a visit to the Scottish Agricultural Museum. The pack is divided into four themes: Here Comes the Present; Out of the Wild; Big Hooze and Cottar Hooze; Man and Beast. Background information is provided, along with suggestions for work at the museum and in class. Some materials would still be useful if a museum visit was not feasible.

The National Museums of Scotland also publishes a series entitled 'Scotland's Past in Action' which includes separate publications on farming, spinning and weaving, sporting Scotland and fishing.

MUSEUM OF SCOTLAND

Situated in Chambers Street, Edinburgh, and opening in 1998, the Museum of Scotland will be the national museum of Scotland's history. It will be an important location for field studies and will feature five core display areas:

- Beginnings: Scotland's Geology and Natural History
- The First Peoples: Scotland in Pre-history
- Kingdom of the Scots: 1100–1707
- North Britain: Scotland Transformed: 1707–1914
- Within Living Memory: Scotland in the Twentieth Century.

Further details can be obtained from:

The Project Office, The Museum of Scotland, Chambers Street, Edinburgh EH1 1JF
Tel: 0131 247 4430.

THE NATIONAL TRUST

The national organisations providing support for field trips are Historic Scotland and the National Trust. The National Trust has produced the following resources to support school visits to many of its properties.

5–14 Resource Packs (photographs, documents, maps, diagrams, etc.)

Preston Mill	£5.00
Robert Smail's Printing Works	£5.00

Study Boxes (artefacts, photographs, documents, oral history accounts)

Study boxes can be loaned to schools for two-week periods. To book a box please contact the property concerned.

Preston Mill (Oct–April only)	No charge
Robert Smail's Printing Works	No charge

Companion Guides

100991	Angus Folk Museum	£1.50
130875	Bannockburn: Kingdom of the Scots, Exhibition	£0.80
101028	Brodie Castle	£1.50
130905	Castle Fraser	£1.50
100311	Culzean Castle	£0.20
100984	Georgian House	£0.80
101004	Gladstone's Land	£0.80
130981	Weaver's Cottage	£1.50

Young Person's Guides

100076	Bannockburn	£1.50
100229	Crathes Castle	£1.50
130974	Gladstone's Land	£0.60
100564	Hill of Tarvit	£0.20

Maps and Charts

100045	Bannockburn Landmark Poster	£2.50
101165	'Kingdom of the Scots' Wall Frieze	£0.95

Full-colour Guidebooks

These are available for most properties and provide a good source of visual material and background information.

Slides (do-it-yourself kits)

Scotland in Trust	£5.00
Countryside in Trust	inc.
St Kilda in Trust	postage
Gardens in Trust	

Videos

		Free hire
The Tenement House, Glasgow	10 mins	postage
Life in the Georgian House 1815	24 mins	£1.50
The New Town	12 mins	per video
The Work of the Weavers	14 mins	
Robert Smail's Printing Works	17 mins	
House of Dun	15 mins	

Resource Packs

The National Trust and Northern College have produced resource packs to support visits to Barry Mill, Angus Folk Museum and House of Dun. The price of each pack is £4.50 and copies can be obtained from: Northern College, Publications Unit, Gardyne Road, Dundee DD1 1NY (Tel: 01382 464278).

For general information and for details on how to order any of the resources listed above see the current National Trust for Scotland publications list. To hire films, videos and slides please contact the Photograph Librarian (Tel: 0131 243 9315).

The address of the National Trust is:

5 Charlotte Street, Edinburgh EH2 4DU
Tel: 0131 226 5922.

Historic Scotland is responsible for many sites of historic importance and a wide range of materials have been produced to support field study visits. The resources described below are listed in alphabetical order by name of location.

Look at the Blackhouse at Arnol

Although very useful as a guide for use during a visit to the Blackhouse in Arnol in the Western Isles, this well-illustrated booklet also provides pupils who are unable to visit with an insight into life in the Highlands and Islands at the beginning of the twentieth century.

Publisher: Bessacarr Prints
Publication Date: 1996
ISBN: 0863842828 (English) 0863842836 (Gaelic)
Cost: £0.75
Medium: Booklet
Pupil Audience: P4–S1

Look at the Border Abbeys

Most useful for pupils who have visited or who are going to visit the monuments, but also a valuable classroom reference for local schools.

Publisher: Bessacarr Prints
Publication Date: 1994
ISBN: 0863841546
Cost: £0.99
Medium: Booklet
Pupil Audience: P4–S1

Caerlaverock Castle Colour Guide

Caerlaverock Castle beside the salt marshes of the Solway Firth is everyone's idea of a 'real' castle. This booklet guides the visitor round the castle and reveals Caerlaverock's stirring history as one of the most important fortresses on the Anglo-Scottish Border. Beautiful colour photographs and reconstruction drawings. A valuable reference for pupils and teachers planning a visit and also useful as a classroom resource on castles.

Author: Grove, Doreen
Publisher: Historic Scotland
Publication Date: 1995
ISBN: 0748008519
Cost: £2.25
Medium: Book
Pupil Audience: P7–S6

Look at Caerlaverock Castle

Primarily intended for use during a visit to the monument, this booklet which is well-illustrated with line drawings, helps pupils to look for interesting features of the monument as they walk round. It would make a useful contribution to a classroom resource bank if accompanied by the *Caerlaverock Castle Colour Guide.*

Publisher: Bessacarr Prints
Publication Date: 1996
ISBN: 0863843212
Cost: £0.75
Medium: Booklet
Pupil Audience: P4–S1

Historic Cumnock

Part of the Scottish Burgh Survey which focuses on areas of archaeological interest to aid developers and town planners when considering further development. Useful reference for local history sources and for information on the development of Cumnock.

Authors, Torrie, Dennison E. P. and Colman, Russell
Publisher: Historic Scotland/Scottish Cultural Press
Publication Date: 1995
ISBN: 1898218404
Cost: £12.95
Medium: Book
Pupil Audience: S4–S6

Dirleton Castle Colour Guide

This booklet guides the visitor around the castle ruins and through the grounds to reveal Dirleton's rich history as one of Scotland's most ancient and remarkable castles. Beautiful colour photographs and construction drawings. A valuable reference for pupils and teachers planning a visit and also useful as a classroom resource on castles.

Author: Grove, Doreen
Publisher: Historic Scotland
Publication Date: 1995
ISBN: 0748010955
Cost: £2.25
Medium: Book
Pupil Audience: P7–S6

Dryburgh Abbey Colour Guide

Dryburgh is one of the four great abbeys built in Scotland's Border country during the Middle Ages. It continues to offer a tranquil place to visit. This colourful guide provides insights into the abbey's fascinating architecture and the absorbing story of the white canons of Dryburgh. Beautiful colour photographs and reconstruction drawings. A valuable reference for pupils and teachers planning a visit and also useful as a classroom resource on abbeys.

Authors: Richardson, James and Wood, Marguerite
Publisher: Historic Scotland
Publication Date: 1996
ISBN: 190016812X
Cost: £2.25
Medium: Book
Pupil Audience: P7–S6

The Abbey and Palace of Dunfermline Colour Guide

The great abbey of Dunfermline has an especially important place in the nation's history. This guide gives a detailed insight into the history and architecture of the abbey which is the final resting place of Saint Margaret, Robert the Bruce and other Scottish kings and queens. Beautiful colour photographs and reconstruction drawings. A valuable reference for pupils and teachers planning a visit and also useful as a classroom resource on abbeys.

Author: Fawcett, Richard
Publisher: Historic Scotland
Publication Date: 1994
ISBN: 0748002812
Cost: £2.25
Medium: Book
Pupil Audience: P7–S6

Dunstaffnage and the Castles of Argyll Colour Guide

In this booklet, Geoffrey Stell explores Argyll's fascinating legacy of castles – who built them, why and when. He guides the visitor around five great castles in the care of Historic Scotland: Sween, Dunstaffnage, Skipness, Kilchurn, and Carnaserie. Beautiful colour photographs and reconstruction drawings. A valuable reference for pupils and teachers planning a visit and also useful as a classroom resource on castles.

Author: Stell, Geoffrey
Publisher: Historic Scotland
Publication Date: 1995
ISBN: 0748004815
Cost: £2.25
Medium: Book
Pupil Audience: P7–S6

Look at East Lothian Castles

Primarily intended for use during a visit to the monuments, this booklet which is well-illustrated with line drawings, helps pupils to look for interesting features of the monuments as they walk round. It would make a useful contribution to a classroom resource bank, particularly for schools in East Lothian.

Publisher: Bessacarr Prints
Publication Date: 1994
ISBN: 0863841570
Cost: £0.75
Medium: Booklet
Pupil Audience: P4–S1

Edinburgh Castle

This book traces the long and complex history of this ancient fortress and discusses all the evidence to produce a full account of how Edinburgh Castle developed and what can still be seen today. Good illustrations and drawings.

Author: MacIvor, Ian
Publisher: Batsford/Historic Scotland
Publication Date: 1993
ISBN: 0713472952
Cost: £14.99
Medium: Book
Pupil Audience: S5–Certificate of Sixth Year Studies

Edinburgh Castle Colour Guide

The royal castle of Edinburgh which for centuries has dominated the city skyline is a powerful symbol of Scotland. This guide takes the visitor on a tour around the castle, explains its architecture, and tells its dramatic history. Beautiful colour photographs and reconstruction drawings. A valuable reference for pupils and teachers planning a visit and also useful as a classroom resource on castles.

Author: Tabraham, Chris
Publisher: Historic Scotland
Publication Date: 1996
ISBN: 074800856X
Cost: £2.25
Medium: Book
Pupil Audience: P7–S6

Look at Edinburgh Castle

Primarily intended for use during a visit to the monument, this booklet which is well-illustrated with line drawings, helps pupils to look for interesting features of the monument as they walk round. It would also be useful in the classroom prior to, or following, a visit, especially if accompanied by the *Edinburgh Castle Colour Guide*.

Publisher: Bessacarr Prints
Publication Date: 1996
ISBN: 0863843247
Cost: £0.99
Medium: Booklet
Pupil Audience: P4–S1

Look at Fort George

Primarily intended for use during a visit to the monument, this booklet which is well-illustrated with line drawings, helps pupils to look for interesting features of the monument as they walk round. It would also make a useful contribution to a classroom resource bank if accompanied by the *Fort George Colour Guide*.

Publisher: Bessacarr Prints
Publication Date: 1996
ISBN: 0863841600
Cost: £0.75
Medium: Booklet
Pupil Audience: P4–S1

Fort George Colour Guide

Fort George, near Inverness, is one of the outstanding artillery fortifications in Europe. It was built as an impregnable fortress for George II's army following the defeat of the Jacobite forces at Culloden in 1746. This guide outlines the story behind the building of Fort George, reveals its subsequent history, and provides a tour of this superlative example of military architecture. Beautiful colour photographs and reconstruction drawings. A valuable reference for pupils and teachers planning a visit and also useful as a classroom resource on castles and forts.

Author: MacIvor, Ian
Publisher: Historic Scotland
Publication Date: 1995
ISBN: 0114934266
Cost: £2.25
Medium: Book
Pupil Audience: P7–S6

Look at Glasgow Cathedral

Most useful for children who have visited or who are going to visit the monument, but also a valuable classroom reference especially for local schools.

Publisher: Bessacarr Prints
Publication Date: 1997
ISBN: 086384331X
Cost: £0.75
Medium: Booklet
Pupil Audience: P4–S1

The Brochs of Gurness and Midhowe Colour Guide

The brochs of Gurness and Midhowe give an interesting insight into Orcadian village life some 2,000 and more years ago. This colourful guide takes the visitor round the broch villages, both excavated in the 1930s, and uses the latest archaeological research to place them in their wider setting. Beautiful colour photographs and reconstruction drawings. A valuable reference for pupils and teachers planning a visit and also useful as a classroom resource on brochs or on life in prehistoric times.

Author: Fojut, Noel
Publisher: Historic Scotland
Publication Date: 1996
ISBN: 0748004661
Cost: £2.25
Medium: Book
Pupil Audience: P7–S6

Historic Hamilton

Part of the Scottish Burgh Survey which focuses on areas of archaeological interest to aid developers and town planners when considering further development. Excellent reference for local history sources and for information on the development of Hamilton.

Authors: Torrie, Dennison E. P. and Colman, Russell
Publisher: Historic Scotland/Scottish Cultural Press
Publication Date: 1995
ISBN: 1898218 42 0
Cost: £14.95
Medium: Book
Pupil Audience: S4–S6

Look at Inchcolm Abbey

Primarily intended for use during a visit to the monument, this booklet which is well-illustrated with line drawings, helps pupils to look for interesting features of the monument as they walk round.

Publisher: Bessacarr Prints
Publication Date: Latest edition 1996
ISBN: 0863841538
Cost: £0.75
Medium: Booklet
Pupil Audience: P4–S1

Jarlshof Colour Guide

At the end of the nineteenth century violent storms ripped open the low cliffs at Jarlshof, at the southern tip of Shetland, to reveal an extraordinary settlement site stretching from late Neolithic times to the seventh century AD. In this guide Patrick Ashmore takes the visitor on a tour of the complex and fascinating settlement at Jarlshof. The guide gives an insight into the way of life of the inhabitants at particularly interesting periods of the site's development – the late Bronze Age, the Iron Age, the Pictish era, the Norse era, and finally the Middle Ages. Beautiful colour photographs and reconstruction drawings. A useful reference for pupils investigating prehistoric times.

Author: Ashmore, Patrick
Publisher: Historic Scotland
Publication Date: 1996
ISBN: 0748004602
Cost: £2.25
Medium: Book
Pupil Audience: P7–S6

Jedburgh Abbey Colour Guide

Built by David I, King of Scots, Jedburgh Abbey is one of the four great Border abbeys. This booklet guides the visitor round the abbey. Beautiful colour photographs and reconstruction drawings. A valuable reference for pupils and teachers planning a visit and also useful as a classroom resource on abbeys.

Author: Fawcett, Richard
Publisher: Historic Scotland
Publication Date: 1996
ISBN: 0748010793
Cost: £2.25
Medium: Book
Pupil Audience: P7–S6

Historic Kirkcaldy

Part of the Scottish Burgh Survey which focuses on areas of archaeological interest to aid developers and town planners when considering further development. Excellent reference for local history sources and for information on the development of Kirkcaldy.

Authors: Torrie, Dennison E. P. and Colman, Russell
Publisher: Historic Scotland/Scottish Cultural Press
Year of Publication: 1995
ISBN: 1898218382
Price: £14.95
Medium: Book
Pupil Audience: S4–S6

Look at Linlithgow Palace

Primarily intended for use during a visit to the monument, this booklet which is well-illustrated with line drawings, helps pupils to look for interesting features of the monument as they walk round. It would make a useful contribution to a classroom resource bank if accompanied by the *Linlithgow Palace Colour Guide*.

Publisher: Bessacarr Prints
Publication Date: Latest edition 1996
ISBN: 0 863841643
Cost: £0.75
Medium: Booklet

Linlithgow Palace Colour Guide

This guide traces the turbulent history of the palace from the early days to the time of the Jacobite uprising and the destruction of the palace by fire in 1746. Beautiful colour photographs and reconstruction drawings. A valuable reference for pupils and teachers planning a visit and also useful as a classroom resource on Scottish castles and palaces.

Author: Pringle, Denys
Publisher: Historic Scotland
Year of Publication: 1996
ISBN: 0748008063
Price: £2.25
Medium: Book
Pupil Audience: P7–S6

Maes Howe Colour Guide

Over 5,000 years old, Maes Howe is the finest chambered tomb in north-west Europe. This guide to the tomb covers its history and many mysteries. Beautiful colour photographs and reconstruction drawings. A valuable reference for pupils and teachers planning a visit, and a useful classroom resource on early people.

Author: Ashmore, Patrick
Publisher: Historic Scotland
Publication Date: 1996
ISBN: 1900168065
Cost: £2.25
Medium: Book
Pupil Audience: P7–S6

Melrose Abbey Colour Guide

Melrose Abbey, in the Scottish Borders, was founded in the twelfth century by the Cistercians. It grew to become one of the wealthiest and most majestic medieval monasteries in Scotland. This booklet guides the visitor round the abbey and gives an insight into one of Britain's most impressive religious houses. Beautiful colour photographs and reconstruction drawings. A valuable reference for pupils and teachers planning a visit and also useful as a classroom resource on abbeys.

Authors: Wood, Marguerite and Richardson, J. S.
Publisher: Historic Scotland
Publication Date: 1995
ISBN: 0748010947
Cost: £2.25
Medium: Book
Pupil Audience: P7–S6

Look at the Orkney Monuments

Primarily intended for use during a visit to the monuments, this booklet which is well-illustrated with line drawings helps pupils to look for interesting features of the monuments as they walk round. Useful in the classroom prior to, or following, a visit and as part of a classroom resource bank, especially if accompanied by the *Skara Brae Colour Guide* and *Skara Brae: A Study of Early Settlers*.

Publisher: Bessacarr Prints
Publication Date: 1994
ISBN: 086384216X
Cost: £0.99
Medium: Booklet
Pupil Audience: P4–S1

Look at St Andrews Castle and Cathedral

Most useful for pupils who have visited or who are going to visit the monuments. It would make a useful contribution to a classroom resource bank if accompanied by the *St Andrews Castle Colour Guide* and *St Andrews Cathedral Colour Guide*.

Publisher: Bessacarr Prints
Publication Date: Latest edition 1996
ISBN: 086384149X
Cost: £0.99
Medium: Booklet
Pupil Audience: P4–S1

St Andrews Castle Colour Guide

This guide tells the story of the castle and explains the architecture of this Episcopal palace, fortress and state prison. Beautiful colour photographs and reconstruction drawings. A valuable reference for pupils and teachers planning a visit, and a useful classroom resource for local schools.

Author: Fawcett, Richard
Publisher: Historic Scotland
Publication Date: 1996
ISBN: 0748005447
Cost: £2.25
Medium: Book
Pupil Audience: P7–S6

St Andrews Cathedral Colour Guide

This colourful guide tells the story of the great cathedral and its associated buildings, and takes the visitor on a tour of the surviving remains. Beautiful colour photographs and reconstruction drawings. A valuable reference for pupils and teachers planning a visit and also useful as a classroom resource on cathedrals.

Author: Fawcett, Richard
Publisher: Historic Scotland
Publication Date: 1996
ISBN: 0748005498
Cost: £2.25
Medium: Book
Pupil Audience: P7–S6

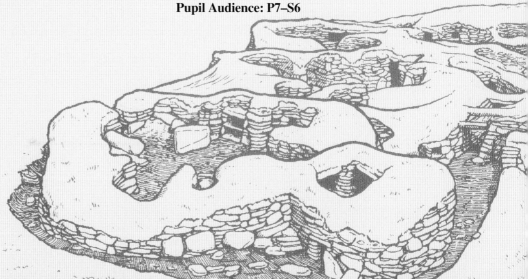

Skara Brae Colour Guide

The prehistoric village of Skara Brae in Orkney, discovered after a wild storm in 1850, was inhabited before the pyramids were built. The structures of this semi-subterranean village survive in impressive condition, and so, amazingly, does the furniture in the village houses. The guidebook is in the form of a tour round the site and the emphasis is on looking at evidence. What is known for certain is printed in bold and what experts believe is printed in italic. Illustrated with colour photographs and reconstruction drawings. A valuable reference for pupils and teachers planning a visit and also useful as a classroom resource on early people. A good accompaniment to the teacher's resource pack *Skara Brae: A Study of Early Settlers.*

Authors: Clarke, David and Maguire, Patrick
Publisher: Historic Scotland
Publication Date: 1996
ISBN: 0748001905
Cost: £2.25
Medium: Book
Pupil Audience: P7–S6

Skara Brae: A Study of Early Settlers

A very useful practical guide to using this significant site with pupils of all ages. Emphasis on progression in 5–14. Although a visit to the site would be appropriate the material can still be used through an investigative approach by classes unable to visit. The pack contains 24 slides, information for primary teachers, photocopiable primary activity sheets, information for secondary teachers, photocopiable secondary information and activity sheets, and assessment materials.

Author: Orkney teachers
Publisher: Historic Scotland
Publication Date: 1997
ISBN: 1900168383
Cost: £15.00
Medium: Resource pack
Pupil Audience: P4–S1

Look at Stirling Castle

Most useful for pupils who have visited or who are going to visit the monument. It would make a useful contribution to a classroom resource bank if accompanied by the *Stirling Castle Colour Guide.*

Publisher: Bessacarr Prints
Publication Date: 1996
ISBN: 0863843034
Cost: £0.75
Medium: Booklet
Pupil Audience: P4–S1

Stirling Castle

Provides the ultimate tour of this remarkable castle which has been the scene of some of the most dramatic events in Scottish history over the centuries. Well-illustrated with reconstruction drawings and photographs.

Author: Fawcett, Richard
Publisher: Batsford/Historic Scotland
Publication Date: 1995
ISBN: 071347623
Cost: £15.99
Medium: Book
Pupil Audience: S5–Certificate of Sixth Year Studies

Stirling Castle Colour Guide

This guide to Stirling Castle is well-illustrated with photographs and reconstruction drawings. A valuable reference for pupils and teachers planning a visit and also useful as a classroom resource on castles.

Author: Fawcett, Richard
Publisher: Historic Scotland
Publication Date: 1996
ISBN: 1900168073
Cost: £2.25
Medium: Book
Pupil Audience: P7–S6

Historic Stranraer

Part of the Scottish Burgh Survey which focuses on areas of archaeological interest to aid developers and town planners when considering further development. A useful reference for local history sources and for information on the development of Stranraer.

Authors: Torrie, Dennison E. P. and Colman, Russell
Publisher: Historic Scotland/Scottish Cultural Press
Publication Date: 1995
ISBN: 1898218412
Cost: £14.95
Medium: Book
Pupil Audience: S4–S6

Tantallon Castle Colour Guide

This guide takes the visitor round the castle ruins and reveals Tantallon's dramatic story as one of the most awesome and impressive of Scotland's castles. Beautiful colour photographs and reconstruction drawings. A valuable reference for pupils and teachers planning a visit and also useful as a classroom resource on castles.

Authors: Tabraham, Chris and Grove, Doreen
Publisher: Historic Scotland
Publication Date: 1995
ISBN: 0748008551
Cost: £2.25
Medium: Book
Pupil Audience: P7–S6

Urquhart Castle Colour Guide

Well-illustrated with colour photographs and reconstruction drawings. A valuable reference for pupils and teachers planning a visit and also useful as a classroom resource on castles.

Authors: Tabraham, Chris and Stewart, Fiona
Publisher: Historic Scotland
Publication Date: 1996
ISBN: 074800601X
Cost: £2.25
Medium: Book
Pupil Audience: P7–S6

School Packs

Intended for use at specific sites and monuments, Historic Scotland school packs provide links to 5–14 Guidelines, ideas for activities prior to and following a visit, activity sheets, historical background and information sheets. Teachers may adapt to suit needs of pupils.

Authors: Various but all qualified teachers
Publisher: Historic Scotland
Publication Date: 1991–7
Cost: £2.50, £4.00
Medium: Information packs with photocopiable activity sheets.
Pupil Audience: P3–P7

The Royal Bank of Scotland, established in 1727, holds over a mile of historical records dating back to the 1660s, and has long been committed to making its archives available to the public through publications and exhibitions.

During the past year the Royal Bank's archivists have been working with Scottish CCC and Lothian Regional Teacher Placement service to develop school workbooks for P5–7 pupils. These are based on the archive collections of the Royal Bank of Scotland, and focus on specific historical contexts as recommended in the Environmental Studies Guidelines. The workbooks can be used either in the classroom, or on a site visit, where 'hands-on', interactive learning is encouraged. Each workbook comes complete with full teacher's notes and suggested pre-visit and follow-up activities. Feedback and evaluation sheets are also provided, along with puzzles and quizzes to test learning outcomes. Three workbooks are currently available.

Jacobite Occupation of Edinburgh

Using contemporary maps, minutes and the diary of the bank's chief cashier – John Campbell – pupils find out about Bonnie Prince Charlie's march into and occupation of Edinburgh, and the role of the bank in the 'Forty-five'. Throughout the site visit, pupils collect evidence about the political sympathies of the chief cashier which can be used to whip up informed debate back in the classroom.

New Town of Edinburgh

This workbook focuses on the reliability of primary sources as evidence for the development and growth of the New Town in Edinburgh. Pupils compare and contrast life in the Old and New Towns, and undertake role play to learn more about the involvement of the Royal Bank in the development of the New Town.

Georgian Edinburgh

Developed in association with the National Trust for Scotland, this workbook is one of three which examines the Georgian period. Pupils visit the Royal Bank where they learn of and see at first hand the work of a Georgian architect in St Andrews Square. A short walking tour highlights the main period features of the New Town. Pupils then visit the National Trust's Georgian House in Charlotte Square, where they study life in a typical town house.

CD-ROM

Available from January 1998 in Acorn, MacIntosh and Windows formats, this CD-ROM was devised and authored by the archivists at The Royal Bank of Scotland, with advice from teachers in Scotland and England. It offers pupils the opportunity to study various historical periods from the Restoration to the twentieth century by looking at the lives of individual people who lived through them.

The CD-ROM is primarily designed to relate to Environmental Studies 5–14, but can also be used for a number of cross-curricular projects. It has a clear and straightforward format, including photographic images, animations, sound, video, text and narration. Teacher's support materials suggest ways of using the CD-ROM, including ideas for extended project and classroom activities and debates.

For more information about these resources and Royal Bank of Scotland Archive Section's education programme, please contact :
Vicki Wilkinson,
Archives Manager,
The Royal Bank of Scotland plc,
Archives Section,
36 St Andrews Square,
Edinburgh EH2 2YB.
Tel: 0131 523 5925.

Section 6

Further Support

The organisations listed below provide support for the teaching of Scottish history. In addition to these organisations the Scottish universities, colleges of education, and education authorities arrange a wide range of conferences and courses on issues relating to the teaching of Scottish history. These include the Certificate of Sixth Year Studies conferences organised by the Department of History at the University of Strathclyde, a degree course in Modern Scottish History jointly delivered by the University of Dundee and the Open University, and the Medieval Higher History conferences held at the University of Glasgow. Through conferences and publications the Scottish CCC also supports Scottish history.

Social and Economic History Society of Scotland

The Social and Economic History Society of Scotland has produced four booklets appropriate for Higher and the Certificate of Sixth Year Studies.

Gray, M.	*Scots on the Move: Scots Migrants 1870–1914*
Payne, P. L.	*Growth and Contraction: Scottish Industry 1860–1890*
Brown, Callum	*The People in the Pews: Religion and Society in Scotland since 1780*
Whatley, C. A.	*Bought and Sold in English Gold: Explaining the Union of 1707*

The address of the Social and Economic History Society of Scotland is given in Section 7.

Scottish Local History Forum

The Scottish Local History Forum publishes a journal entitled *Learning and Teaching Local History* which contains articles relevant to local history. The Scottish Local History Forum can be contacted through:

Mrs Chantal Hamill, The Secretary, Scottish Local History Forum, 128 Gowan Bank, Livingstone EH54 6EW

Scottish Education Advisers Liaison Group for Social Subjects

The Scottish Education Advisers Liaison Group for Social Subjects (SEALC) has members from a range of interested bodies including the education authorities, universities, colleges of education, HM Inspectors of Schools and the Scottish CCC. One function of SEALC is to disseminate resources which are not commercially available. SEALC can be contacted through:

The President, Jan Ward, Adviser, North Ayrshire, Cunningham House, Irvine, Ayrshire KA12 8EE
or

The Secretary, Peter Hillis, Head of Social Studies, University of Strathclyde Faculty of Education, Jordanhill Campus, 76 Southbrae Drive, Glasgow G13 1PP.

Scottish Association of Teachers of History

The Scottish Association of Teachers of History (SATH) is the national organisation representing Scottish history teachers. The current President of SATH is Elizabeth Trueland, Principal Teacher of History, Mary Erskine School, Ravelston, Edinburgh EH4 3NT.

In addition to organising conferences for history teachers, SATH produces three publications: *History Teaching Review, Resources Review* and *The Bulletin. History Teaching Review* features content-based articles on topics relating to existing syllabuses, *Resources Review* contains reviews on a wide range of published resources and *The Bulletin* comprises tried and tested classroom materials. SATH can be contacted either at http://www.Strath.ac.uk/Departments/SSE/Hist/SATH or through:

The Secretary, SATH, Eastwood High School, Capelrig Road, Newton Mearns, Glasgow G77 9UQ.

Obtaining Resources

Aberdeen City Education Offices
(Contact: Mrs Doris Mayor)
Summerhill Education Centre
Stronsay Drive
Aberdeen
AB15 6JA
Tel: 01224 208662
Fax: 01224 208671

Addison Wesley Longman Ltd
Edinburgh Gate
Harlow
Essex
CM20 2JE
Tel: 01279 623636
Fax: 01279 431059

Argyll Publishing
Glendaruel
Colintraive
Argyll
PA22 3AE
Tel: 01369 820229
Fax: 01369 820229

BBC Education
Broadcasting House
5 Queen Street
Edinburgh
EH2 1JF
Tel: 0131 248 4261
Fax: 0131 248 4267

BBC Enterprises Ltd
Woodlands
80 Wood Lane
London
W12 0TT
Tel: 0181 576 2570
Fax: 0181 749 8766

Bessacarr Prints
Thackray House
Manor Road
Hatfield
Doncaster
South Yorkshire
DN7 6SD
Tel: 01302 351112
Fax: 01302 351158

C. B. Publishing Ltd
18 Lochlann Terrace
Culloden
Inverness
IV1 2P2

Canongate Books Ltd
14 High Street
Edinburgh
EH1 1TE
Tel: 0131 557 5111
Fax: 0131 557 5211

Channel 4 Learning Ltd
Castle House
75-76 Wells Street
London
W1P 3RE
Tel: 0171 580 8181
Fax: 0171 580 9350

Channel 4 Schools
74 Victoria Crescent Road
Dowanhill
Glasgow
G12 9JL
Tel: 0141 357 2446

Channel 4 Schools
P.O. Box 100
Warwick
CV34 6TZ
Tel: 01926 433333
Fax: 01926 450178

Dunedin Multimedia Ltd
69 Merchiston Crescent
Edinburgh
EH10 5AQ
Tel: 0131 229 1737

Education and Social History Society of Scotland
Department of History
John Anderson Campus
University of Strathclyde
16 Richmond Street
Glasgow
G1 1XQ
Tel: 0141 552 4400
Fax: 0141 552 0775

Franklin Watts
96 Leonard Street
London
EC2A 4RH
Tel: 0171 739 2929
Fax: 0171 739 2318

Glasgow City Archives
Mitchell Library
North Street
Glasgow
G3 7DN
Tel: 0141 287 2999
Fax: 0141 287 2815

Hamilton Publishing
10-16 Colvilles Place
Kelvin Industrial Estate
East Kilbride
Glasgow
G75 0SN
Tel: 01335 233081

Heinemann Educational Publishers
Halley Court
Jordan Hill
Oxford
OX2 8EJ
Tel: 01865 314301
Fax: 01865 314029

HMSO
See under The Stationery Office

Historic Scotland
Longmore House
Salisbury Place
Edinburgh
EH9 1SH
Tel: 0131 668 8652 or 668 8732
Fax: 0131 668 8903

Hodder & Stoughton Ltd
338 Euston Road
London
NW1 3BH
Tel: 0171 873 6000
Fax: 0171 873 6024

Imprint Publishing Systems
8 Braehead Avenue
Milngavie
Glasgow
G62 6DJ
Tel: 0141 956 5300

National Museums of Scotland
Chambers Street
Edinburgh
EH1 1JF
Tel: 0131 225 7534
Fax: 0131 220 4819

The National Trust
5 Charlotte Street
Edinburgh
EH2 4DU
Tel: 0131 226 5922

Northern College of Education
Gardyne Road
Broughty Ferry
Dundee
DD5 1NY
Tel: 01382 464000
Fax: 01382 464900

Oliver and Boyd
See under Addison Wesley Longman Ltd

Pulse Publications
45 Raith Road
Fenwick
Kilmarnock
Ayrshire
KA3 6DB
Tel: 01560 600832
Fax: 01560 600832

Royal Bank of Scotland plc
Archives Section
36 St Andrews Square
Edinburgh
EH2 2YB
Tel: 0131 523 5925

Scottish Assocation of Teachers of History (SATH)
c/o University of Strathclyde
Jordanhill Campus, Faculty of Education
Social Studies Education Department
76 Southbrae Drive
Glasgow
G13 1PP
Tel: 0141 950 3395
Fax: 0141 950 3268

Scottish Borders Education Department
Council Headquarters
Newtown St Boswells
Melrose
TD6 0SA
Tel: 01835 824000
Fax: 01835 822145

Scottish Centre for Information and Library Services
Scottish Library Association
1 John Street
Hamilton
ML3 7EU
Tel: 01698 458888
Fax: 01698 458899

Scottish Children's Press
Unit 4
Leith Walk Business Centre
130 Leith Walk
Edinburgh
EH6 5DT
Tel: 0131 555 5950
Fax: 0131 555 5018

**Scottish Consultative Council on the Curriculum
(Scottish CCC)**
Gardyne Road
Broughty Ferry
Dundee
DD5 1NY
Tel: 01382 455053
Fax: 01382 455046

Scottish Council for Educational Technology (SCET)
74 Victoria Crescent Road
Dowanhill
Glasgow
G12 9JL
Tel: 0141 337 5000
Fax: 0141 337 5050

Scottish Medievalists
c/o Department of Medieval Studies
University of St Andrews
St Andrews
KY16 9LS

Orders: Scottish Book Source
137 Dundee Street
Edinburgh
EH11 1BG
Tel: 0131 229 6800
Fax: 0131 229 9070

Scottish Museums Council
County House
20/22 Torphichen Street
Edinburgh
EH3 8JB
Tel: 0131 229 7465
Fax: 0131 229 2728

Scottish Record Office
HM General Register House
Edinburgh
EH1 3YY
Tel: 0131 535 1314
Fax: 0131 535 1360

Social and Economic History Society of Scotland
Department of History
University of Strathclyde
McCance Building
Richmond Street
Glasgow
G1 1XQ
Tel: 0141 552 4400
Fax: 0141 552 0775

Stanley Thornes (Publishers) Ltd
Ellenborough House
Wellington Street
Cheltenham
GL50 1YD
Tel: 01242 228888
Fax: 01242 221914

Stationery Office, The (Headquarters)
Publications Centre
PO Box 276
London
SW8 5DT
Tel: 0171 873 9090
Fax: 0171 873 8463

Stationery Office, The (Scottish Branch)
21 South Gyle Crescent
Edinburgh
EH12 9EB
Tel: 0131 479 3141
Fax: 0131 479 3142

Tuckwell Press Ltd
The Mill House
Phantassie
East Linton
EH40 3DG
Tel/Fax: 01620 860164

University of Strathclyde
Faculty of Education
Jordanhill Campus
76 Southbrae Drive
Glasgow
G13 1PP
Tel: 0141 950 3000
Fax: 0141 950 3268

Wayland Publishers Ltd
61 Western Road
Hove
East Sussex
BN3 1JD
Tel: 01273 722561
Fax: 01273 723526

Index: Resource Titles and Series